QUEST

Early History of Israel

Exodus – Joshua

formerly God's People - God's Land

STUDENT WORKBOOK

AUTHOR
MARNI SHIDELER McKENZIE

EDITORS
MRS. NELLIE E. CONSTANCE
MRS. LOIS EADES, M.A.
MRS. JEAN POLK
MRS. RITA HOWELL

COVER ART & GRAPHIC DESIGN
TROY D. RUSSELL

PROJECT EDITOR
TOM M. CONSTANCE JR.

EXPLORER'S BIBLE STUDY
P.O. BOX 425
DICKSON, TN 37056-0425

*We believe the Bible is God's Word, a divine revelation, in the original language
verbally inspired in its entirety, and that it is the supreme infallible authority
in all matters of faith and conduct.*
(2 Peter 1:21; 2 Timothy 3:16)

Printed in the United States of America

Published by Explorer's Bible Study
2652 Hwy. 46 South
P.O. Box 425
Dickson, TN 37056-0425
1-800-657-2874

www.explorerbiblestudy.org

Contents

About the Author

Marni Shideler McKenzie is married to William H. McKenzie, III. They live in Batesville, Mississippi, where Bill is in private law practice. They have three children, Melanie, William, and Joanna, and are active in community efforts and the ministries of their local church. Marni attended the University of Mississippi as a Carrier Scholar and received B.A. and M.A. degrees in English. While in college, Marni became serious in her efforts to nurture her relationship with Jesus Christ, and began to study the Bible carefully. She "retired" from a brief high school teaching career when their children were born and has used her spare time ever since for organizing or teaching Bible study classes to adults and children. She credits her husband for giving her the freedom to study Scripture and the opportunity to teach Explorer's Bible Study classes continually since 1979.

Marni has written the **Quest** courses **Early History of Israel: Exodus through Joshua, Promises Fulfilled: Luke & Acts, Words of Wisdom: Job, Psalms and Proverbs,** and **God's Perfect Plan: Exploring Bible Prophecy from Genesis to Revelation** for Jr. and Sr. High students. In addition to Quest, Marni has written an illustrated children's book, **An Alphabet of Bible Creatures,** and a 12-part study series for adults on the Apostles Creed entitled **The Creed and the Christian**. She is also the author of our adult curriculum courses, **God's Perfect Plan: Exploring Bible Prophecy from Genesis to Revelation** and **Romans, Galatians and James**.

Bibliography

A great debt is owed the many Bible authorities whose writings have been used as a resource in writing and preparing this material.

A Note to Parents and Teachers

If you have said "yes" to the call of God to teach, you have accepted one of the most important challenges in building the future kingdom. In James 3:1 we read *". . .let not many of you become teachers, knowing that we shall receive a stricter judgment."* It takes a great commitment to put yourself in a place of responsibility in which children and adults will make life-changing decisions based on the life and teaching you put before them. But knowing the high expectations God has for those who commit to this calling should not deter you from this wonderful and powerful opportunity to serve in this way. As you see the loving response to God from a child or student, it is difficult - if not impossible - to imagine NOT teaching! It becomes a compelling urgency that God rewards in so many ways that you'll wonder why there was ever a question mark after the words, "Should I consider teaching?"

Whether you are a homeschooling parent, a Sunday School teacher, or a Christian educator, God has chosen you to teach! As a teacher, you will have a great influence in the lives of your children or students. You have been given the responsibility by God to mentor these lives spiritually. It is an awesome responsibility but you don't have to do it alone! God is with you every step of the way.

Teach each child faithfully, prayerfully and consistently in His Word: know it, believe it, live it, and then teach it. Teaching is impossible without the first three. We hope this Bible curriculum will help guide you through this process.

A guide for those who are called to teach. A Teacher must have:

1. A personal commitment to Christ.

2. A love for students with a desire to see them understand the Word of God.

3. A call to the ministry through God's Word.

4. A personal commitment to daily Bible study and to completing the lesson each week.

"And these words which I command you today shall be in your heart. You shall teach them diligently to your children, and shall talk of them when you sit in your house, when you walk by the way, when you lie down, and when you rise up."
Deuteronomy 6:6-7

A Note to the Student
How to Use this Workbook

You are about to embark on a great adventure - the study of God's Word. We have called this study **Quest** because you will be on a quest for knowledge, understanding and application of the many wonderful truths found in the world's most read book - the Bible.

As you begin each lesson, pause to pray for the Holy Spirit to guide you as you seek the treasures to be found in the Word. There is no need to use anything but your Bible in answering your questions. Commentaries and study notes in your Bible can be helpful, but the goal of this study is for you to discover what God wants to communicate to **YOU** through the lesson. After you have completed your lesson you may wish to go back and read a Bible commentary to further clarify what you have studied.

Daily Questions: Work the assigned questions each day. The discipline of daily Bible study will soon become part of your regular routine. You will find that the questions are challenging, interesting, and fun to do!

Lesson Notes: You will find helpful insight and ways to personally apply what you have studied in the "notes" section of your lesson.

Bible Journal and Memory
We suggest that you get a spiral notebook or 3-ring binder and keep a Bible journal of your study of Early History of Israel: Exodus - Joshua. You will find this elephant symbol throughout your lessons, along with reference(s) for **suggested** memory verses. Some lessons have more verses included in the suggested memory than most students will be able to learn in one week. We suggest that you look through the verses listed and select the ones that you feel you would like to memorize. Even though you may be unable to memorize all of the suggested verses, we recommend that you write them all in your Bible journal and do your best to master as many as you can each week. Writing the verses will make it easier for you to memorize. You may also want to use your Bible journal to write down important things that you have learned as you study your lesson. . . or use a page to illustrate a story from a lesson. Be CREATIVE!

Your word I have hidden in my heart, that I might not sin against You!

Psalm 119:11

As you study. . .

1. Pray that God will give you understanding.

2. Find out what the Bible says.

3. Choose to live God's way every day.

4. Never stop learning and growing. . .there is always MORE!

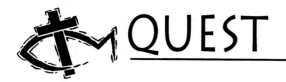 **QUEST**

How much do you know?

Before you begin your study of EARLY HISTORY OF ISRAEL, let's take a pop quiz to test your Bible knowledge. Since this test is designed to find out what you know right now, answer the questions without using your Bible. To find out how well you did, look at the answers printed on page 2. Don't be discouraged if you miss a few. Before the end of your study of EARLY HISTORY OF ISRAEL, you will know the answer to every one of these questions!

1. In order to control the population of the Jews, Pharaoh decided to
   a) subject them to severe and cruel slavery.
   b) order the midwives to kill every male Hebrew child.
   c) issue an order that all Hebrew sons should be cast into the Nile River.
   d) all of the above

2. Moses was how old when he was called by God to lead the children of Israel out of Egypt?
   a) 40 years old
   b) 26 years old
   c) 80 years old
   d) about as old as Charlton Heston was when he played the part

3. When God appeared to him in a burning bush, Moses
   a) took off his sandals.
   b) told God to find someone else to do the job.
   c) told God that he couldn't go because he had a speech impediment.
   d) all of the above
   e) none of the above

4. Pharaoh refused to let the children of Israel leave Egypt because
   a) he had hardened his heart towards God.
   b) he had hardening of the arteries.
   c) he had a hard time understanding the request.
   d) he was hard of hearing.

5. In the first of the ten plagues, God caused the water of this river to turn to blood:
   a) the Euphrates River.
   b) the Tigris River.
   c) the Nile River.
   d) the Mississippi River.

6. The children of Israel crossed the Red Sea on
   a) a fleet of barges that they had tied at the dock.
   b) the Golden Gate Bridge.
   c) dry land with a wall of water on either side.
   d) baskets woven from reeds and sealed with tar.

7. God provided food for his people while they were in the desert. The people called it manna which means
   a) "God has provided us food."
   b) "What is it?"
   c) "food from heaven."
   d) "tastes like bagels, lox and cream cheese."

8. When the people needed water in the desert, Moses
   a) had each tribe dig a well.
   b) applied to the Sinai Water District for a hook-up.
   c) at God's command, struck a rock and water flowed out of it.

9. The ark of the covenant that God commanded Moses to construct contained
   a) the broken tablets of the Law that Moses had thrown down when he saw the people worshiping a golden calf.
   b) two tables of the Ten Commandments, a pot of manna and Aaron's rod.
   c) Aaron's rod and the Ten Commandments.
   d) the Ten Commandments and a pot of manna.

10. When the people sinned by worshiping a golden calf, Moses
    a) sent all those who had worshiped it back to Egypt.
    b) had those who had worshiped it flogged.
    c) burned it in the fire, ground it into powder, mixed it with water, and made the people drink it.
    d) none of the above

11. In the book of Leviticus, God commanded that the land be allowed to rest (no planting, reaping or pruning)
    a) every 17 years.
    b) every 70 years.
    c) every 7 years.
    d) whenever crop production levels dropped below government standards.
    e) whenever Congress ordered it.

12. The beginning of the book of Numbers records a census (counting or numbering) of God's people. When another census was taken 38 years later
    a) the population had nearly doubled in size.
    b) because of the hardships in the desert, the number had decreased by about 10%.
    c) the number was nearly the same.
    d) the number was exactly the same.

13. Moses sent twelve spies to Canaan to look at the land. When they returned, 10 of the spies reported that
    a) the land was flowing with milk and honey.
    b) there were grasshoppers in the land.
    c) the people of the land looked like grasshoppers.
    d) there were giants in the land; "We were like grasshoppers in our own sight."

14. In the book of Numbers, when the people complained about having only manna to eat, God
    a) made them eat quail till it came out of their nostrils.
    b) ordered Moses to sacrifice a ram and give it to the people for food.
    c) told them to quit complaining and eat the manna.

15. When Balaam went to prophesy against Israel, the Angel of the Lord opposed him. Balaam then
    a) beat his donkey with a stick.
    b) heard his donkey say "What have I done to you to make you beat me?"
    c) saw the Angel of the Lord standing before him with his sword drawn.
    d) all of the above
    e) none of the above

16. The name "Deuteronomy" means
    a) "duet or composition for two performers."
    b) "second law."
    c) "our wanderings are over."
    d) "God will provide for His people."
    e) none of the above

17. According to the law given to Moses by God, included in the exemptions from military service and warfare were
    a) men who had built a new house.
    b) men who had planted a new vineyard.
    c) men who were newly married.
    d) men who were faint-hearted.
    e) all of the above

18. When Joshua sent two spies into Jericho, they escaped capture with the help of a
    a) blind beggar at the city gate.
    b) group of well-placed business men who hoped to profit from the deal.
    c) prostitute who later became an ancestor of Christ.
    d) rebel band of Roman soldiers.

19. God ordered the Israelites to march around Jericho
    a) 7 times every day for a week.
    b) 7 times.
    c) once each day for 6 days and 7 times on the 7th day.
    d) one time for each tribe of Israel (12 times).

20. At the battle of Gibeon, in order to give victory to Joshua and the Israelites, God
    a) caused the sun and moon to stand still for a whole day.
    b) sent hail from the sky to drive their enemies out.
    c) struck their enemies blind.
    d) sent fire from heaven to consume their enemies.

ANSWERS:
1. d	2. c	3. d
4. a	5. c	6. c
7. b	8. c	9. b
10. c	11. c	12. c
13. d	14. a	15. d
16. b	17. e	18. c
19. c	20. a & b	

Notes

The Book of Exodus

Introduction The book of **Exodus** begins with the children of Israel wanting to EXIT or depart from Egypt. The book of Genesis had recorded their happy entry into Egypt years earlier as invited guests of the ruler or pharaoh of that land. Then, they were merely the extended family of Jacob (or Israel, as God re-named him). [See Genesis 32:28.] They were 70 men strong, accompanied by wives, children, servants, and livestock. They had come at Pharaoh's invitation because their brother Joseph had saved Egypt and the surrounding peoples by obeying God and storing up food for a predicted famine. Blessed by God, over a period of 400 years, the twelve branches of Israel's family tree had produced approximately two million people. However, the early chapters of Exodus record how unwelcome and unhappy a group they had become. They wanted out; they needed a deliverer; and God revealed His man and His plan for their grand escape.

What Is Included in the Book of Exodus? The book of Exodus records the events of 360 years—the interval between the death of Joseph and the giving of the law at Sinai. During this time there was a rapid increase of the people due to the blessing of God upon them. In brief, the content of this wonderful book of Exodus is as follows:

1) The alarm of the Egyptian pharaoh over the population increase of Israel.
2) Pharaoh's evil plans for stopping this growth and the failure of those plans.
3) The circumstances surrounding the birth and education of Moses.
4) Moses' first impulsive attempt to defend Israel from Egypt's cruelty.
5) God's selection of Moses to be the deliverer of His nation.
6) Moses' interaction with Pharaoh about the release of Israel.
7) The ten plagues which ultimately broke Pharaoh's resistance.
8) The first Passover and Israel's dramatic exit.
9) Pharaoh's decision to follow with his army.
10) The miraculous crossing of the Red Sea to Sinai.
11) The giving of the Ten Commandments, the **law**, and the acceptance of the "Book of the **Covenant**" by the people.
12) Israel's sin of **idolatry** and its punishment.
13) The pattern for the construction of the **tabernacle**.
14) The laws concerning religious life.

Exodus - departure or out going

Blessed by God, over a period of 400 years, the twelve branches of Israel's family tree had produced approximately two million people. However, the early chapters of Exodus record how unwelcome and unhappy a group they had become.

law - a rule of conduct ordered and enforced by an authority

covenant - formal, solemn, and binding agreement

idolatry - the worship of a material object as a god

tabernacle - large tent used as the central place of worship

Preserved in this exciting book are the great facts about the early history of Israel, this family-turned-nation.

More than History

Preserved in this exciting book are the great facts about the early history of Israel, this family-turned-nation. But more than a record of history, it is a record of miracles. How God worked in these miracles throughout Israel's history is a pattern by which He still works in the **redemption** of all people. For example, without Christ, all men are in slavery to Satan and sin, just like the people of Israel were the slaves of Pharaoh. As Moses was sent to deal with Pharaoh and lead them to freedom, so Jesus came to be our Savior and Deliverer. Further, in the journey through the wilderness there is a picture of the Christian's journey through life: unsurrendered, murmuring, stumbling, wandering, longing for the things left behind, dissatisfied and powerless. How often have the blessings intended for us been cut off because of this same rebellious behavior? True, like Israel, many have been saved from slavery, but they still refuse to go forward to Canaan, the place of the surrendered Christian life, which is Spirit-filled and controlled, and through which God can work.

redemption - the act of buying back; liberation through purchase

Who Wrote the Book of Exodus?

Jewish tradition credits Moses with the authorship of the first five books of the Bible: Genesis, Exodus, Leviticus, Numbers and Deuteronomy, which are called the **Pentateuch**. In Luke 24:44, Christ definitely credits Moses with writing the Pentateuch. (Compare also the following: Mark 12:26 with Exodus 3:2-5; Matthew 8:3-4 with Leviticus 14:1-7; Matthew 19:7-8 with Deuteronomy 24:1-4.)

Pentateuch - first five books of the Bible (penta=five)

Why Is It Important to Study the Old Testament ?

We are told in the New Testament that if we love God, we will keep His commandments (John 14:15). But how can we obey Him if we don't know what He says? We must study His Word. This Bible study takes the view that the books of the Old and New Testaments are the **infallible** Word of God, communicated to men selected from the people of Israel for this purpose. This traditional or historical view of the Bible holds that certain holy men of old spoke as they were moved by the Holy Spirit. Therefore, the Bible does not contain just the religious ideas of the **Hebrew** race, but the teachings of God Himself. The Bible is not just a wonderful piece of literature but the true Word of God to mankind. From Genesis to Revelation, the Bible teaches that there is only one true God; this belief is called **monotheism**. From the beginning to the end it contains the promise and the **doctrine of a Redeemer** and of redemption. The Old Testament tells of a God who cared about the world He created, even when that world repeatedly turned away from His love.

infallible - incapable of error

Hebrew - synonym for Israelite, from a word meaning "from the other side"

monotheism - belief in one god (mono=one; theo=god)

doctrine of a Redeemer - teaching about a Savior

In Genesis, the truth about God was given to mankind. Over the years, the true knowledge was corrupted, changed, and mishandled and gave birth to the many different religious beliefs seen today. Man started with the truth of God and exchanged it for many lies. *"For since the creation of the world His invisible attributes are clearly seen, being understood by the things that are made, even His eternal power and Godhead, so that they are without excuse, because although they knew God, they did not glorify Him as God, nor were thankful, but became futile in their thoughts, and their foolish hearts were darkened"* (Romans 1:20,21). In summary, the historical or traditional view of the Bible, that is followed in our study, holds that the Old Testament is a revelation—God showing man about Himself, His plan, and His purposes. It is <u>not</u> an evolution—man slowly figuring out for himself what kind of religion he needs or what kind of god or gods he serves. Since God inspired the writing of the Bible, we can trust its message.

We will be learning many lessons from these Old Testament books that will prove to be a great blessing. Familiar Bible stories will deepen in meaning as they are studied in their full **context**, and the New Testament teachings of Jesus will begin to make more sense. But perhaps, best of all, we will be drawn closer to the true God, who still works powerfully in the lives of people and nations who turn to Him.

> **context** - the parts of a passage that surround the word or phrase that can throw light upon its meaning.

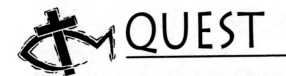

QUEST

Questions

Study Procedure: Read the Scripture references before answering questions. Unless otherwise instructed, use the Bible only in answering questions. Some questions may be more difficult than others but try to answer as many as you can. Pray for God's wisdom and understanding as you study and don't be discouraged if some answers are not obvious at first. Do not read the study notes for this lesson until AFTER you have completed your questions.

Day One: Vocabulary: Matching

_____1. context

_____2. covenant

_____3. doctrine of a Redeemer

_____4. Exodus

_____5. Hebrew

_____6. idolatry

_____7. infallible

_____8. law

_____9. monotheism

_____10. Pentateuch

_____11. redemption

_____12. tabernacle

a) departure or outgoing

b) formal, solemn, and binding agreement

c) the parts of a passage that surround the word or phrase that can throw light upon its meaning

d) synonym for Israelite from a word meaning "from the other side"

e) a rule of conduct ordered and enforced by an authority

f) the worship of a material object as a god

g) large tent used as the central place of worship

h) belief in one god

i) the act of buying back; liberation through purchase

j) incapable of error

k) teaching about a Savior

l) first five books of the Bible

Day Two: Read Exodus 1

MEMORY: EXODUS 1:7

1. List the 12 sons of Jacob. _____

_____

_____

2. What verses tell when and why Israel became unpopular in Egypt? _____

3. What methods were used to stop their population growth? Did they work?_____

_____

_____

_____

_____

_____

4. None of this was a surprise to God. He had told Abraham at least 600 years earlier about the
    future of this family.

    a) Read Genesis 15:13-14 and tell what was prophesied. _____

    _____

    _____

    b) What part of this had already come to pass in Exodus 1? _____

    _____

5. Read Genesis 45:17-28 and Genesis 47:1-6. Locate on your map where the Israelites lived before
    their move to Egypt and where in Egypt they were settled.

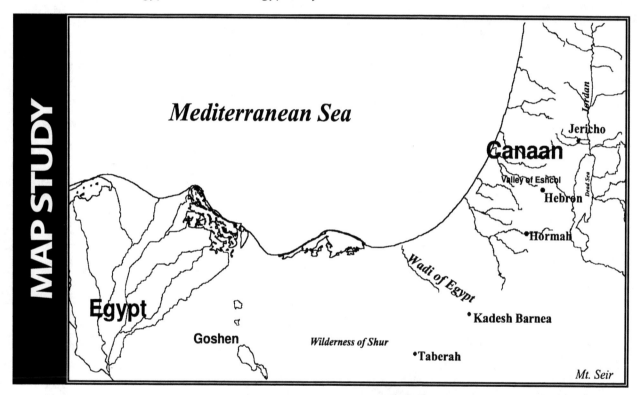

Day Three: Read Exodus 2:1-10 and Hebrews 11:23  *MEMORY: EXODUS 2:10*

1. Describe how one mother responded to the population control efforts of Pharaoh.

    _____

    _____

    _____

2. Is effort or the use of imaginative means inconsistent with faith? Explain your answer.

    _____

    _____

    _____

    _____

3. a) What name was given to the child? _____

   b) What did it mean? _____

   c) Who named him? _____

4. List some interesting facts about this account that show the wonderful way God prepared
   to bring forth a leader to deliver Israel from Egypt. _____
   _____

Day Four: Continue in Exodus 2; read Acts 7: 20-23   **MEMORY: PSALM 29:1-2**

   1. **Challenge Question:**

      a) Who had the child during the early, formative years? (Give references to support your
         answer.) _____
         _____
         _____

      b) Can we learn a valuable lesson from this in regard to the future of our own children?
         _____
         _____

   2. What advantages did Moses have as the son of Pharaoh's daughter that were not available to
      children of Hebrew slaves? (Read Acts 7:20-23.) _____
      _____

   3. In your opinion, what was the reason Moses reacted the way he did to the Egyptian's beating the
      Hebrew? _____
      _____
      _____
      _____

   4. What else do you think he needed to learn before he could become an effective leader for
      Israel? _____
      _____
      _____

Day Five: Read Hebrews 11:24-27   **MEMORY: HEBREWS 11:1**

   1. a) What choice did Moses make?
      _____
      _____

b) What was the result of this choice? _____

_____

_____

c) What similar choices are you called to make each day? _____

_____

_____

2. Read Genesis 25:1-6. Who were the Midianites? _____

_____

_____

3. List at least three interesting things that happened to Moses in Midian. _____

_____

_____

4. From Exodus 2:23-25, give evidence that God cared about Israel._____

_____

5. Reflecting on these two chapters, what are some lessons we can learn about

   a) motherhood? _____

   _____

   b) human nature?_____

   _____

   c) God? _____

   _____

6. Now take a few minutes to read your study notes for this lesson.

Notes

Who Will Help Us? — Birth of a Helper

Introduction The book of Exodus opened where Genesis finished, with the enlarged family of Jacob (renamed Israel) victimized by famine, looking to the vast food storages of Egypt for relief. On arrival, through a series of God-directed events, they were reunited with their brother Joseph, whom they had sold into slavery years before. His faithfulness to God had brought him up the ladder of national leadership to a place second only to Pharaoh. What the brothers had meant for evil, God had certainly used for good. Joseph, obedient to the direction of God years before, was in the position to save not only Egypt, but also the lives of his unsuspecting family. While in Egypt, this family of seventy men, with their wives, children, extended relations, and servants, would live separately from the general Egyptian population in the fertile area of Goshen. Their separation served two purposes: first, it kept them from mixing with the Egyptians, who despised their chief occupation as shepherds, and secondly, it served God's purpose of pulling them away from the idolatry of Canaan, while multiplying their population in fulfillment of His promises to Abraham in Genesis 12 and 15. In Egypt they were kept a separate people, but, in the space of four centuries, they became a powerful people.

In Egypt they were kept a separate people, but, in the space of four centuries, they became a powerful people.

The Death of Joseph
Exodus 1:6

Joseph entered Egypt as a slave when he was only seventeen, but he was blessed with power and splendor as Pharaoh's chief officer. He lived 71 years after his family came to join him in Egypt and died at the age of 110. According to Hebrews 11:22, *"By faith Joseph, when he was dying, made mention of the departure of the children of Israel, and gave instructions concerning his bones."* Joseph trusted God to fulfill all His promises to Israel, and, even at his death, he asked that his bones be taken for burial in Canaan to which, in God's timing, they would surely return. The family of Israel continued to thrive in Egypt after Joseph's death, and 278 years passed before the birth of Moses.

Oppression of Israel in Egypt
Exodus 1:7-22

(Exodus 1:7) Exactly how much the population had grown was not recorded here, but the writer of Exodus used four words or phrases to express the fact that the multiplication was great: they were *"fruitful and increased abundantly, multiplied and grew exceedingly mighty."* It was this population explosion that made Egypt nervous about Israel's impact on its country. Over the decades, the helpful actions of Joseph had faded from royal memory and with them any obligation to give special treatment to the children of Israel. But God was still in control of even these circumstances. He would fulfill the promise to Jacob in Genesis 46:3-4, *"...do not fear to go down to Egypt, for I will make of you a great nation there. I will go down with you to Egypt, and I will also surely bring you up again."*

A Fearful King
Exodus 1:8-10

The reference to a "new king" quite possibly meant more than just "another king;" there probably had been a change of **dynasty**. Historians referred to this king, who persecuted the children of Israel, as the "Pharaoh of the Oppression," placing him in the nineteenth dynasty during the reign of the shepherd kings. Most

dynasty - a succession of rulers of the same line of descent

Egyptologists held that Ramses II and his son, Menephtah, were the pharaohs of the oppression and the exodus. Their combined reigns, according to secular history, corresponded with the length of the persecution indicated in the Bible, and their personalities with the Biblical accounts of the cruel treatment of the Israelites. The "supply cities" of Pithom and Ramses (verse 11), which the Israelites built for that pharaoh, have been excavated. Discovered chambers were not only very well-constructed, but also divided by partitions eight to ten feet in thickness, made of sunbaked bricks, some with and some without straw.

The Real Enemy "Fear"

The fast population growth of Israel while in Egypt alarmed the pharaoh, but he did not want to lose them since they were a useful people. He just wanted to make sure he could control them so that they would not unite to oppose his government or leave to join another power. Actually, Israel was a quiet group, happy to live peacefully, keeping their flocks and herds in Egypt's fertile land. However, fear of what might happen drove that pharaoh to his extreme methods of slowing the population growth of Israel.

Fear always grows powerful where faith in the true God is absent. That is a truth we all need to recognize. The greatest horrors of history have been caused by people motivated by fear. Are you overwhelmed by certain fears? Are others victims because you give in to those fears? Over and over in Scripture it is repeated, *"Fear not."* The perfect love of God can cast away all fear (1 John 4:18). *"For God has not given us a spirit of fear, but of power and of love and of a sound mind"* (2 Timothy 1:7). Come to God and confess your fears. Increase your time in Bible study and prayer. Faith comes by hearing the Word of God, and where faith comes, fear must leave.

Faith comes by hearing the Word of God, and where faith comes, fear must leave.

The Bondage
Exodus 1:11-14

Under the scorching sun, Hebrew slaves, bleeding from cruel beatings, were made to *"serve with rigor"* and their lives were *"bitter with hard bondage."* God had promised Abraham an extraordinary increase in the number of his descendants, and He would not permit a crafty and cruel king to interfere with His eternal promises. So the more Pharaoh and his subjects abused them, *"the more they multiplied and grew."* It is good for us to remember at this crucial period of history that Christians are never at the mercy of their enemies. God has the power to turn the wisdom of the world into foolishness, upset all human schemes, and make every step taken to oppose His will useful in fulfilling it.

A Deadly Law
Exodus 1:15-22

When cruel slavery failed to slow the growth of the Israelites, Pharaoh adopted a measure even more evil. He ordered the midwives to put to death every male child born to an Israelite woman. The **midwives** *"feared God, and did not do as the king of Egypt commanded them, but saved the male children alive."* (Exodus 1:17) When charged by Pharaoh with disobeying orders, they made the excuse that the Israelite women were so strong that they had their babies before the midwives could assist. *"Therefore God dealt well with the midwives,"* not for their deception, but for their courage in defying Pharaoh. They were blessed by God with households and families of their own.

> **midwives** - women who assist other women in childbirth

Pharaoh did not quit there. He gave another order to all the people that all sons born to Hebrew women should be cast into the Nile River. How long this command was in effect we do not know. The situation of Israel grew desperate. If they were to survive, a deliverer would have to emerge.

A son was born to them who would become the deliverer of their people, and it would be that people, in God's good time, who would produce a greater Deliverer, a Savior, for the whole world.

The Birth of Moses
Exodus 2:1-10

(Exodus 2:1-4) A man and wife of the tribe of Levi were among the Hebrew slaves of Egypt. A son was born to them who would become the deliverer of their people, and it would be that people, in God's good time, who would produce a greater Deliverer, a Savior, for the whole world.

Because of Pharaoh's evil law for population control, Israel's future deliverer needed delivering himself. His rescue involved a mother's love, a baby's cry, compassion of a princess, and the shrewdness of a sister. Though a slave, his mother dared to defy Pharaoh's orders and hid Moses for three months. When she could no longer hide the baby in her home, she wove and water-proofed a basket, placed the baby in it, and *"laid it in the reeds by the river's bank."* She stationed his sister nearby to guard him. More than clever, the family of Moses was full of faith in God. Hebrews 11:23 records, *"By faith Moses, when he was born, was hidden three months by his parents, because they saw he was a beautiful child; and they were not afraid of the king's command."* The family of Moses did its part, but God more than supplied what was lacking to accomplish His purposes.

Pharaoh Pays the Bills
Exodus 2:5-10

Throughout the Bible, the history of Israel was interwoven with the history of the **Gentile** world. Earlier in the recorded life of Joseph, and now in the story of Moses, the salvation of Israel was always connected with the reactions of the Gentiles. The daughter of the same king who wanted to destroy the Hebrews was used by God to be the protector of their future leader. God was at work. His **providence** brought the king's daughter to the river, gave

> **Gentile** - not Jewish

> **providence** - divine guidance or care

her the compassion and courage to save the Hebrew child, and stopped her from questioning his parentage or such a quick provision of a Hebrew nurse. The beautiful faith of Moses' mother was rewarded: she received her child again and even received wages for caring for him until he was weaned and was taken into the palace of Pharaoh. Satan's plan was spoiled by his own weapon, as the very instrument he was using to frustrate the purpose of God was used by God to nourish and bring up Moses, through whom God would defeat the power of Satan.

Leader in Training
Hebrews 11:24-27; Acts 7:20-29

There were three periods in the training of Moses to prepare him for the work to which God had called him: first, in the home of his parents, next, in the court of the Egyptian king, and finally in the desert of Midian. Moses recorded no incidents of his life during these years. His purpose was not to write his biography but to give an account of God's dealings with His people.

At Home

Without doubt, his early training in the home of his parents was the most important. From parents who had expressed such great faith, he surely learned of the traditions of his people and the promise of God through their father Abraham to deliver them out of Egypt. Established in the heart of this young child was the foundation of faith that would support the building of a life of obedient service to God.

Established in the heart of this young child was the foundation of faith that would support the building of a life of obedient service to God.

How important it is that we do not underestimate the value of influencing our little ones in the things of God early in life. The Bible instructs us to *"train up a child in the way he should go"* (Proverbs 22:6). This does not mean that we should wait until he gets old enough to choose for himself. Parents have a solemn responsibility before God in the religious education of their children. It is in the early years of a child's life that character is molded.

In Egypt and Midian

Stephen, in his Spirit-given message in the book of Acts, chapter seven, said that *"Moses was learned in all the wisdom of the Egyptians."* Thus Moses knew Israel's oppressor—all the pride, power and cruelty of Egypt. He had learned the wisdom of Egypt, but he also needed to learn the wisdom of God. The third period of training for Moses was spent in Midian. Here God prepared him, through an **ascetic** and strenuous life-style, for the great task of being a ruler and a deliverer of his people.

He had learned the wisdom of Egypt, but he also needed to learn the wisdom of God.

ascetic - practicing severe self-denial as a means of spiritual discipline

Would-be Deliverer
Exodus 2:11-12;
Hebrews 11:24-27

There came a time in the life of Moses when he had to make a choice. To remain in the Egyptian court as the son of Pharaoh's daughter with all of the pleasures, riches, and power would have been the easier way. He chose rather to suffer with the children of God, having faith in God's promises. The education of Moses in the Egyptian court could not make him forget that he belonged to the people of Israel.

oppressive - unreasonably burdensome or severe

Moses looked on his people's **oppressive** burdens and was moved to give them help. He *"saw an Egyptian beating a Hebrew,"* and filled with indignation at the cruel treatment of the taskmaster beating a helpless Hebrew, he acted in the capacity of a judge and ruler over this situation. In self-will and **presumption**, he attempted a deliverance before God's time. Killing an Egyptian who was mistreating a Hebrew was not God's way of solving the problem.

presumption - acting without full knowledge of a situation

Peacemaker
Exodus 2:13-15a

Moses returned to the area the next day. He saw two Hebrews arguing, and attempted to act as a peacemaker, urging **reconciliation**. However, because they viewed his murder of the Egyptian the day before as an act of cruel power rather than an attempt to protect slaves, they refused his advice. When Moses realized his previous action had been exposed, he was afraid and left Egypt to avoid Pharaoh's certain retribution. Israel was not yet ready to be delivered.

reconciliation - restoration of friendship or harmony

Fugitive
Exodus 2:15b-25

God removed Moses from Egypt to the land of Midian in the Sinai desert, where, in the solitude and desolation of that environment, he would be trained in divine wisdom. The Midianites were descendants of Abraham and Keturah (Genesis 25:1-5). They, as a people, did not embrace the worship of the true and living God, but certain individuals kept faith in Him. Jethro, Moses' father-in-law, was such a man. He was the priest and prince of Midian, and he treated Moses kindly, giving him a home and a wife from among his daughters. There in Midian Moses became the husband of a simple shepherdess and the father of two sons: Gershom (meaning "stranger in a strange land") and Eliezer ("God is my help").

God removed Moses from Egypt to the land of Midian in the Sinai desert, where, in the solitude and desolation of that environment, he would be trained in divine wisdom.

Moses could never have led Israel in the wilderness without the experience of Midian. His knowledge of language, his extensive schooling, and his city life would have been of little value without the advanced education afforded by this internship in the rugged life of a desert shepherd. In the meantime, God had not forgotten His people still enslaved in the land of Egypt. *"God heard their groaning, and God remembered His covenant with Abraham."*

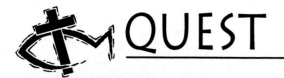 # QUEST

Questions

Study Procedure: Read the Scripture references before answering questions. Unless otherwise instructed, use the Bible only in answering questions. Some questions may be more difficult than others but try to answer as many as you can. Pray for God's wisdom and understanding as you study and don't be discouraged if some answers are not obvious at first. Do not read the study notes for this lesson until AFTER you have completed your questions.

Day One: Vocabulary: Matching

_____1. ascetic

_____2. dynasty

_____3. Gentile

_____4. midwives

_____5. oppressive

_____6. presumption

_____7. providence

_____8. reconciliation

a) acting without full knowledge of a situation

b) restoration of friendship or harmony

c) a succession of rulers of the same line of descent

d) not Jewish

e) women who assist other women in childbirth

f) practicing severe self-denial as a means of spiritual discipline

g) unreasonably burdensome or severe

h) divine guidance or care

9. What did you find most interesting about last week's lesson? _____

_____

_____

10. From Exodus 2, list the life-changing events Moses experienced. _____

_____

_____

_____

MEMORY: PSALM 29:3-4

Day Two: Read Exodus 3

1. Exodus 3:2 refers to Moses looking. What did he see? _____

_____

2. Give some incidents from modern history that would remind us of Israel's suffering in Egypt.

_____

_____

3. Read Exodus 3:4-6 and list the things Moses did in this situation. _____

_____

_____

4. a) What made this place "holy ground"? _____

_____

b) Has there been an experience with God in your life that made you feel you were on "holy
ground"? Explain. _____

_____

MEMORY: EXODUS 3:7-8

Day Three:

1. a) Complete the phrases from verses 7 and 8 of Exodus 3 that tell of God's concern for His

people? *"I have surely* _____ *who are in*

Egypt, and have _____*because of their taskmasters, for I*

_____ *. So, I have* _____

them out of the hand of the Egyptians, and to _____

to a good and large land, to a land flowing with milk and honey...."

b) What do you personally learn about God from these verses? _____

_____

_____

2. Read the call of God to Moses in Exodus 3:10. Name some things Moses learned about God

before his call. _____

_____

_____

3. Do you think Moses' response to the call of God was due to a sense of his own weakness?

Explain your answer. _____

_____

_____

4. How do you respond when you feel called to a difficult job? _____

_____

_____

Day Four:

1. What two doubts did Moses express to God? _____

_____

2. What response did God give to each one? _____

_____

_____

3. Read Exodus 4. What were the next two doubts Moses expressed? _____

_____

_____

4. a) Did Moses want God to forget the whole thing or just let someone else do it? _____

_____

   b) Have you been guilty of this when you were asked to serve in some difficult capacity?

_____

_____

MEMORY: EXODUS 4:10-12

Day Five:

1. What signs did God give Moses to strengthen his faith and trust? _____

_____

_____

2. What was God's solution for Moses' last excuse? _____

_____

3. Verses 18-23 describe Moses' preparations for leaving Midian and going to Egypt. What new information does God give him in these verses? _____

_____

_____

4. **Challenge Question:** What can we learn from the incident recorded in verses 24-26 of Exodus 4?

_____

_____

5. Moses was not the only one being used by God. From verses 27-31 of Exodus 4 record what you discover about Aaron. _____

_____

_____

6. Now take a few minutes to read your study notes for this lesson.

Notes

Moses Called into Service

The Burning Bush Exodus 3:1-6	Moses spent the first forty years of his life as an Egyptian prince, the second forty years as a Midian shepherd, and the last forty years as a desert leader for the newly-

While his earlier education in warfare and government would help in the future of a freed Israel, only a thorough knowledge of frontier life would enable him to lead them out of Egypt and through their difficult desert experiences.

nomadic - having no fixed or permanent residence; wandering

At times we probably all have felt buried in a desert. We have looked for a way to escape our ordinary living.

organized nation of Israel. About those middle years, there was little recorded except the fact that he married, had two sons, and managed the flocks of his father-in-law Jethro, the priest of Midian. However, in God's strategy, the Midian experience provided Moses with knowledge he could never have gained in the palace life of Egypt's pharaoh. While his earlier education in warfare and government would help in the future of a freed Israel, only a thorough knowledge of frontier life would enable him to lead them out of Egypt and through their difficult desert experiences. He needed the training he gained from life with **nomadic** people to find food and drink and trails in the wilderness. This education in the rugged life was essential for his success as God's hand-picked leader.

At times we probably all have felt buried in a desert. Our daily routine has bored us and we dreamed about bigger and better things we might be doing. We have looked for a way to escape our ordinary living. Maybe we have dreamed of serving God in Africa or India as missionaries, but we have not yet noticed the friend or neighbor who needs God now. Let us learn a lesson from this part of the life of Moses: faithfulness right now in our present situation at home, school, or work will be the best preparation for a future, perhaps greater, ministry.

At the age of eighty, under the very shadow of Mt. Sinai where he would afterwards receive the Law, Moses encountered the presence of God in a bush that was burning yet not consumed. It was at this moment that God called him by name. The burning bush not consumed could well represent the children of Israel. For over 400 years they had been in Egypt, and at the time of this encounter they were under severe hardship. What nation in all of history could have survived the persecution Israel had? The miraculous power of God worked to preserve His people, and from them He would bring a Redeemer to save the whole world.

Orient - the eastern portion of the world

Holy Ground
Exodus 3:5-6

When Moses knew the presence of God had to do with the miracle, he did not ask about the meaning of the burning bush. The voice which called his name was the voice of the Lord, and Moses heard the solemn command: *"Do not draw near this place. Take your sandals off your feet, for the place where you stand is holy ground."* The removal of the shoes or sandals was required when entering a place of worship in the **Orient**. It was a symbolic act, still practiced today, representing the removal of the uncleanness caused by contact with the world. Holiness was required of one who would worship a holy God. Moses showed even more reverence by covering his face: *"He was afraid to look upon God."* Would God teach us a lesson today about how we should come before Him to worship whether in our homes or in a sanctuary? God has not changed. He is still the God of Abraham, Isaac and Jacob. He demands **dignity** and **reverence** when we come into His presence. Moses obeyed God's instructions for proper worship with his outward actions, and it is still appropriate today to be respectful in approaching God.

dignity - good taste in conduct or appearance, orderliness

reverence - honor or respect felt or shown

God's Plan

All of Israel had cried to God for help in escaping the terrible situation in Egypt, but they were not sure God had heard. So, before informing Moses of his appointment to leadership, God assured him that not only was He completely aware of Israel's pain, but He also had an immediate plan to help them get out of Egypt and back into the land they had been promised. But God planned more than just a great escape; He promised glory and blessing for Israel in Canaan.

Moses' Response

After God announced that Moses had been selected to go back and approach Pharaoh about Israel's release, Moses tried to disqualify himself and cried, *"Who am I, that I should go?"* What a change had taken place in the attitude of this one who, as a young nobleman in the court of the king, felt quite able to deliver his people! What a difference in being a shepherd in the wilderness and being an ambassador to a king and a leader of men! Humility was a good characteristic for a leader if it allowed him to trust more fully in God. However, if humility were not balanced with confidence in God's ability to provide, it could result in self-pity, which would block the flow of God's power.

Humility was a good characteristic for a leader if it allowed him to trust more fully in God. However, if humility were not balanced with confidence in God's ability to provide, it could result in self-pity, which would block the flow of God's power.

God's Promises

God replied to Moses, *"I will certainly be with you."* The "I" of Moses was met with the "I" of God. If God be for us, who can be against us? What assurance for this chosen servant of God, and for us as well!

God added another promise in verse 12: *"When you have brought the people out of Egypt, you shall serve God on this mountain."* Little did Moses realize what this promise would mean to him in the future. Their future gathering around the smoking mountain would be a memorable one. For Moses it would mean forty days and forty nights alone with God for the receiving of God's law and the pattern for the construction of the tabernacle. For the people it would mean a dramatic change in their knowledge of, **obligations** to, and trust in God.

obligations - duties

self-existent - existing without any outside help

eternal - everlasting; without end

God's Name
Exodus 3:13-15

Only God can say "I am." We are what God makes us and what He enables us to be. What God is now, He always will be. God can never be greater or less than He is. "I am" includes all God can be; He is **self-existent**, changeless, **eternal**. He is not the

Only God can say "I am." We are what God makes us and what He enables us to be.

"I am" includes all God can be; He is self-existent, changeless, eternal. He is not the creation of man's imagination.

elders - having authority by virtue of age and experience

sacred - set apart for the service or worship of God

creation of man's imagination. He is the Deliverer, the Redeeming God. This God was One who cared for His people, One who heard their cry, and One who was to be their Savior. In such a God they could put their trust, and they could accept Moses as His chosen messenger.

The Mission and the Message
Exodus 3:16-22

Moses was to gather together the **elders** of the tribes of Israel and explain to them his mission and God's promises. Then, the elders were to accompany Moses as he went to deliver his message to Pharaoh. The message was to be a request for Pharaoh to permit the children of Israel to go on a three-day journey into the wilderness to sacrifice to the Lord. This was to be a fair test of the attitude of Pharaoh. It was expected that Pharaoh would refuse at first and, as a result, have to face the consequences for opposing God. After enough of God's power was displayed, Pharaoh would, in the end, change his mind, and Israel would leave with a bonus of expensive gifts.

The Messenger
Exodus 4:1-9

Even though God made the instructions plain, Moses was still reluctant to accept his job. The patient love of God was displayed as Moses was given three signs designed to encourage him as well as prove to the elders that God had approved him as messenger. These were the first recorded miracles of **sacred** history:

1. **His shepherd's staff became a serpent.** The simple rod of the shepherd was to become powerful for destruction and would prove more powerful than the scepter of the king.

2. **His hand became leprous.** Leprosy was a dreaded contagious and incurable disease that caused nerve endings to die. The infected person then would hurt himself without knowing it, continuing to use the injured limb or other area. The untreated, damaged area would become infected or useless, and permanent disfigurement and disability would occur. Anyone having the disease had to live apart from everyone else. One of the symptoms was a patch of dead, white skin. The miracle of the leprous hand illustrated God's power to inflict punishment or to heal and save.

3. **The water from the Nile would be changed to blood when poured on the ground.** The River Nile was Egypt's life-line for drinking, bathing, fishing, and travel. God's power could change it to a place of death.

The Messenger's Mouth
Exodus 4:10-17

Moses felt inadequate for this big task. He tried to excuse himself by pointing out his weaknesses. *"I am not eloquent....I am slow of speech and slow of tongue."* With great patience God allowed him to speak, meeting each excuse with a promise and assurance of strength.

God still has an answer to every doubt, a promise for every fear, a generous supply for every want, and divine strength for every human weakness. We can be encouraged as we study the life of Moses and perhaps identify with attitudes of fear and doubt we find. The love, grace, patience and mercy of God go beyond what we can comprehend. May God teach us complete faith and trust in Him. He wants us to know that He is able and willing to show His power in the little concerns of our life as well as in the great challenges.

He wants us to know that He is able and willing to show His power in the little concerns of our life as well as in the great challenges.

Assistant Allowed

Moses did not accept the will of God for himself as leader even after God answered every excuse with a promise: "Please send someone else," he urged, revealing a stubbornness that did not please God. *"So the anger of the Lord was kindled against Moses."* But even at this time, God did not leave him or excuse him. God took away his last difficulty by giving him an assistant, his own brother Aaron. He would become the helper and companion that Moses needed. Finally, an obedient Moses asked and received permission from his father-in-law to leave Midian and return to Egypt.

Three Meetings
Exodus 4:24-31

First Meeting (Exodus 4:24-26) Moses had neglected to have his youngest son **circumcised**, a sign regarded as a seal of the covenant of God with His people. *"It came to pass on the way...that the Lord met him and sought to kill him."* How strange but how effective a lesson! Moses could not be disobedient to the basic directions of God for his family and be allowed to lead Israel in a life of national obedience. Holiness begins at home. His wife, not very cheerfully, performed the neglected religious requirement, and the life of Moses was spared.

circumcised - "to cut around" As a personal sign that each male child was in covenant with God, the foreskin of the penis was to be cut away when the child was eight days old.

Second Meeting (Exodus 4:27-28) At the foot of Mt. Sinai there was a touching reunion of Moses and Aaron. Here they spent time together talking about how they could fulfill their great mission and be used of God to deliver their people from the Egyptian oppressor.

Moses could not be disobedient to the basic directions of God for his family and be allowed to lead Israel in a life of national obedience. Holiness begins at home.

Third Meeting (Exodus 4:29-31) The leaders and people were persuaded to accept Moses and Aaron as their divinely appointed leaders. They believed when they heard that the Lord had visited the children of Israel, and they worshiped. God's plan for Israel's deliverance was off to a good start.

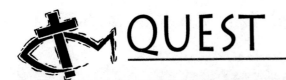 QUEST

Questions

Study Procedure: Read the Scripture references before answering questions. Unless otherwise instructed, use the Bible only in answering questions. Some questions may be more difficult than others but try to answer as many as you can. Pray for God's wisdom and understanding as you study and don't be discouraged if some answers are not obvious at first. Do not read the study notes for this lesson until AFTER you have completed your questions.

Day One: Vocabulary: Matching

_____1. elders

_____2. Orient

_____3. sacred

_____4. self-existent

_____5. eternal

_____6. reverence

_____7. nomadic

_____8. circumcise

_____9. dignity

_____10. obligations

a) the eastern portion of the world

b) honor or respect felt or shown

c) "to cut around"; a personal sign that each male child was in covenant with God; the foreskin of the penis was to be cut away when the the child was eight days old

d) set apart for the service or worship of God

e) existing without any outside help

f) good taste in conduct or appearance; orderliness

g) having authority by virtue of age and experience

h) everlasting; without end

i) having no fixed or permanent residence; wandering

j) duties

11. Write down two things you learned from last week's lesson that you could apply in your own life.

a) _____

_____

b) _____

_____

MEMORY: PSALM 29:11

Day Two: Read Exodus 5

1. Based on what he says in the following verses, describe Pharaoh's attitude

a) toward God in verse 2: _____

b) toward Moses and Aaron in verse 4: _____

c) toward the people in verses 6-9: _____

2. Moses was prepared for the refusal of Pharaoh to let the people go, but what had he not expected

a) from Pharaoh? _____

_____

b) from the officers of the children of Israel? _____

_____

3. Was the situation helped when the officers went to appeal to Pharaoh for mercy? _____

4. When things got worse instead of better, Moses was upset.

    a) What did he do? _____

    b) What can you learn from this? _____

Day Three: Read Exodus 6

MEMORY: EXODUS 6:2-4

1. In answer to Moses' prayer, did God change His plan?

  In your opinion, why or why not?

  _____

  _____

2. From verses 6-8 in Exodus 6, write out the phrases that have the words "I will."

    a) I will _____

    b) I will _____

    c) I will _____

    d) I will _____

    e) I will _____

    f) I will _____

    g) I will _____

    Challenge: Can you list any New Testament promises that are similar to these?

    _____

    _____

3. When Moses took this word from God back to the people, what was their response and why?

  _____

Day Four: Chapters 7-12 should be read together since they describe the ten plagues God sent on Egypt. It will help if you scan the remaining questions first, so that you can note the information needed as you read.

  Fill in the blanks in the chart below:

Number	Plague	Reference	Effect	Responses
First	Water to blood	7:14-24	_____	_____
			_____	_____
			_____	_____
Second	Frogs	_____	_____	_____
			_____	_____
			_____	_____
			_____	_____

Number	Plague	Reference	Effect	Responses
Third	_____	8:16-19	Lice on man and beast.	Magicians couldn't duplicate it. Admitted that God had done it. Pharaoh's heart grew hard; no repentance.
Fourth	Flies	8:20-32	_____ _____ _____ _____	_____ _____ _____ _____ _____
Fifth	Disease on livestock	_____	_____ _____ _____	_____ _____ _____
Sixth	_____	_____	_____ _____ _____	_____ _____ _____ _____ _____
Seventh	Huge hail with fire	9:13-35	Some feared and took cover for their animals; others didn't. Terrible destruction of life and crops. Goshen was not hurt.	_____ _____ _____ _____ _____
Eighth	_____	_____	_____ _____ _____ _____	_____ _____ _____ _____
Ninth	Darkness	10:21-29	Darkness that could be felt over Egypt for 3 days but not in Goshen.	_____ _____ _____ _____ _____
Tenth	_____	_____	_____ _____ _____	_____ _____ _____

Day Five:

MEMORY: PSALM 30:1

1. In Exodus 5:2 Pharaoh asked, *"Who is the Lord that I should obey His voice to let Israel go?"* From Exodus 7:1-6, how did God plan to answer him?

_____

_____

_____

2. Every time Pharaoh "almost" changed his mind, he offered a compromise to Moses. Each one pictured a kind of temptation that we still face today in serving God whole-heartedly in front of an unbelieving world.   For each compromise listed, put in your own words, how we face a similar compromise today. (The first one is done for you.)

   a) Exodus 8:25: *"Go, sacrifice to your God in [this] land."* Often we want to compromise with the ways of the world around us. We worship on Sunday but live like heathens the rest of the week. Satan tells us not to go overboard: "Stay in the world. Don't try to be so different."

   b) Exodus 8:28: *"I will let you go, that you may sacrifice to the Lord your God in the wilderness; only you shall not go very far away."* _____

   _____

   _____

   _____

   c) Exodus 10:8-10: *"Go, serve the Lord your God. Who are the ones that are going? (Moses replies, "Everyone and everything we own.") Pharaoh says, "The Lord had better be with you when I let you and your little ones go! Beware, for evil is ahead of you. Not so! Go now, you who are men, and serve the Lord..."* _____

   _____

   _____

   _____

   _____

   d) Exodus 10:24: *"Go, serve the Lord; only let your flocks and your herds be kept back. Let your little ones also go with you."* _____

   _____

   _____

   _____

3. Now take a few minutes to read **your** study notes for this lesson.

Notes

God Sends Moses to Pharaoh

Off to a Good Start
Exodus 5-11

Moses and Aaron met with the leadership of Israel, repeated God's promise of help, and performed the supernatural signs. The response was recorded this way: *"So the people believed; and when they heard that the Lord had visited the children of Israel and that He had looked on their affliction, then they bowed their heads and worshiped."* So far, so good. With the people united in support, Moses and Aaron appeared before Pharaoh.

ego - from the word for "I," the self in contrast to the world or others

The kings of Egypt probably held an open court in which any one might appear to ask for justice or for a particular favor. Moses and Aaron took their turn before this throne to ask that their people be released from work to go and offer sacrifices to their God. The Egyptians worshiped many gods, so this request would not have been unusual. However, the words, *"Thus says the Lord God of Israel: 'Let My people go,'"* would have been extremely irritating to this cruel, proud king. After all, in Egypt, the ruling pharaoh was considered to be a powerful god himself. His reply revealed his wounded **ego**: *"Who is the Lord, that I should obey His voice....I do not know the Lord, nor will I let Israel go."*

Pride keeps us ignorant since we refuse to be taught, and blind to our own weaknesses because we refuse to examine our own lives.

Royal Pride

Pharaoh did not know, much less believe or fear, their God. After all, he must have thought, how strong could He be, if He were the God of slaves? Self-centered pride was an ugly characteristic of Egypt's leader. Pride grows when we think too highly of ourselves and forget the importance of others. Pride keeps us ignorant since we refuse to be taught, and blind to our own weaknesses because we refuse to examine our own lives. Pharaoh's pride kept him blind and ignorant to any power beside his own, but God, through a chain of difficult circumstances, broke that **arrogant** heart and made a terrific display to the world of His own superior abilities in the process. Just as the pharaoh before him had unknowingly housed and educated his future enemy Moses, this pharaoh was about to provide the opportunity for his own gods to be shown worthless against the God of Israel's matchless power.

arrogant - exaggerating one's own worth or importance

Bad to Worse

However, the display of power God planned would require some additional time. Moses and the leaders of Israel were quite disturbed when this first audience with Pharaoh resulted in an increase of their hard labor instead of expected relief. "Bricks without straw" were to be produced at the same rate as when all materials were provided. The phrase became a proverb for unreasonable cruelty throughout the ages.

Blaming Game

This harsh setback caused the people to criticize and lose faith in Moses' and Aaron's leadership. They had not realized the full power of their slavemaster until they tried to get free. For the Christian, it is still this way. The strength of the bad habit, addiction, or influence is felt most strongly when we are determined to let God free us from it.

Moses prayed honestly to God about his heartfelt doubts and his shock at the cruel reaction of Pharaoh. We must be honest in our prayers to God, since He knows what we are feeling anyway. Moses was not punished or criticized by God for asking. The epistle writer James expressed this in James 1:5: *"If any of you lacks wisdom, let him ask of God, who gives to all **liberally** and without **reproach**, and it will be given to him."* God clearly had not been surprised by what had happened in the first meeting. He reassured Moses that this was opening up the way for a terrific display of strength on God's part. God wanted Moses, as He wants us, to focus not on the circumstances around us but on God Himself, on His reliability and power. We, like Moses, are only required to obey His next order; God will handle all the details.

> *We must be honest in our prayers to God, since He knows what we are feeling anyway.*

liberally - generously, freely

reproach - rebuke; to bring into discredit

Pep Talk

God did offer some encouragement to His **dejected** messenger. He reminded Moses of the covenant that He had made with Israel, and He gave a clear picture of just what He intended to do for these people He loved:

dejected - depressed; downcast

1. *"I will bring you out from under the burden of the Egyptians."*
2. *"I will rescue you from their bondage."*
3. *"I will redeem you with an outstretched arm."*
4. *"I will take you as My people."*
5. *"I will be your God."*
6. *"I will bring you into the land which I swore to give to Abraham, Isaac, and Jacob."*
7. *"I will give it to you as a heritage."*

God cannot lie, so whatever He promised He would back up with action. That is the way He operated in the past, and this is the way He operates now and always. What great news! No situation right now is too difficult for Him to handle. No power over you is greater than His power to set you free. What do you need today? Tell God in prayer, ask and wait for His next direction, and then obey. He is responsible for the end result; you are responsible for present faithful obedience.

Thinking Like Slaves
Exodus 6:9-13

It was not strange that the message given to Moses for the people fell on deaf ears. They had heard golden promises from him before but had witnessed only the increase of misery and distress. *"They did not heed Moses, because of anguish of spirit and cruel bondage."* The long-term effect of slavery was revealed in that response. They had lived so long as slaves without courage or self-respect that they did not even try to be strong after their first hopes were crushed. Yet before God gave them freedom, He had to make them capable of freedom. God moved ahead as if He had not heard their unbelieving complaints. This time Moses was not to go before Pharaoh with a request but with a demand that he let the people go out of the land. Again distressed, Moses spoke before the Lord. The people hadn't listened to him, so how could he expect Pharaoh to listen? Moses, looking at himself instead of to God, doubted his ability to persuade Pharaoh.

They had lived so long as slaves without courage or self-respect that they did not even try to be strong after their first hopes were crushed. Yet before God gave them freedom, He had to make them capable of freedom.

A Pause for Identification
Exodus 6:14-27

A bit abruptly, a genealogy of Moses and Aaron was inserted. Their direct ancestor Levi was the third of Jacob's twelve sons (Genesis 49). Moses and Aaron may not have felt very significant, but God knew what He would do with these two faithful servants of His. He had their biographical information recorded for future generations to examine.

Orders Repeated
Exodus 6:28-7:2

Moses was in a difficult situation. He was being sent to perform a task at which he had previously failed. The general situation with the people he wanted to help had grown worse. To go back to Pharaoh was like rowing against wind and tide with little hope of reaching shore. Such discouragement led Moses to exaggerate his difficulties and to resort to an old excuse about poor speaking abilities. He was afraid he would fail in delivering the message. However, God already knew the weaknesses of Moses and promised him power and authority that even Pharaoh would have to respect.

This is true today. We go forth as His servants, not in our own power, but by the power of the Holy Spirit, and we speak in His name and with His authority. In 1 Thessalonians 1:5 we note that the gospel came not *"in word only, but also in power, and in the Holy Spirit and in much assurance."* Our job is to obey; God will provide the power and protection as we go.

The Problem of Heart Hardening
Exodus 7:3-11:10

Twenty times in this section, *"hardening"* was mentioned in connection with Pharaoh's heart. The three Hebrew words for hardening used here meant "to make firm or **insensible**," "to make heavy or

insensible - incapable of feeling or sensation

unimpressionable," or "to make stiff or **immovable**." Half of these references pointed to Pharaoh as causing the hardening and half referred to God. Before the ten plagues, when Aaron first turned the rod into a serpent, the heart of Pharaoh was hardened by himself. After each of the first five plagues the hardening was attributed to Pharaoh himself. Not until after the sixth plague, with Pharaoh still resisting, was it recorded that *"the Lord hardened the heart of Pharaoh" (Exodus 9:12).*

| **immovable** - one that cannot be moved |

For Pharaoh, every act of disobedience made obedience more difficult. This should serve as a warning to us today. Every time we choose our own will over God's will we widen the gap between us, making His voice or vision more distant and easier to disregard the next time. This sort of hardening is just as sure to bring judgment as it was in the case of Pharaoh.

Every time we choose our own will over God's will we widen the gap between us, making His voice or vision more distant and easier to disregard the next time.

| **God's Power Shown** Exodus 7:14-11:10 |

Each time Pharaoh refused to obey God's Word, God responded with a plague. There was a double purpose in this:

1. *"And the Egyptians shall know that I am the Lord, when I stretch out My hand on Egypt and bring out the children of Israel from among them"* (Exodus 7:5).

2. *"And that you may tell in the hearing of your son and your son's son the mighty things I have done in Egypt"* (Exodus 10:2).

All the world, believers and non-believers, would have clear evidence of the power of Almighty God.

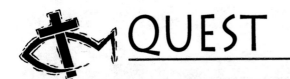 **QUEST**

Questions

Study Procedure: Read the Scripture references before answering questions. Unless otherwise instructed, use the Bible only in answering questions. Some questions may be more difficult than others but try to answer as many as you can. Pray for God's wisdom and understanding as you study and don't be discouraged if some answers are not obvious at first. Do not read the study notes for this lesson until AFTER you have completed your questions.

Day One: Fill in the blank using the words below for vocabulary review:

arrogant   immovable

dejected   liberally

ego   reproach

insensible

1. God does not _____ those who ask Him for advice; He gives _____ to those who ask.

2. Pharaoh's over-sized _____ caused his _____ attitude toward the requests of Moses.

3. Moses felt _____ after Pharaoh increased the people's burdens.

4. Pharaoh seemed _____ to the sufferings of others.

5. What may seem to be an _____ obstacle for man, is never too difficult for God.

6. From last week's lesson, select one situation from Moses' life with which you could identify and tell why. _____

_____

_____

_____

_____

MEMORY: PSALM 32:1,8-10

Day Two: Read Exodus 11 and 12: The Tenth Plague

1. In Exodus 11:1-3, God assured Moses that the tenth plague would bring the release of Israel.

   What instructions did God give the Israelites in these verses and why? _____

   _____

   _____

   _____

   _____

2. In Chapters 11 and 12 the first "Passover" is described. It is a powerful picture of what God planned to do for us through Christ to free us from our slavery to sin, Satan, and self. Supply the information requested below from Exodus 11 and 12.

   a) Date of selection of sacrificial animal: _____

      Date of sacrifice: _____

   b) Describe the sacrificial animal: _____

   c) What was done with the blood and for what purpose? _____

      _____

      _____

      _____

   d) What was done with the rest of the animal?_____

      _____

   e) How often and with what changes was this to be repeated later? _____

      _____

      _____

MEMORY: PSALM 33:4

Day Three: New Testament References to Passover

1. Read Luke 22:19-20. What Christian observance originated with the Passover service?

   _____

2. Read the following New Testament passages and underline any words or phrases that refer to the Passover instructions in Exodus. Write down the reference from Exodus to which it relates in the blank provided.

   a) 1 Corinthians 5:7 - "*Therefore purge out the old leaven, that you may be a new lump, since you truly are unleavened. For indeed Christ, our Passover, was sacrificed for us.*"

      _____

   b) 1 Peter 1:18-19 - "*Knowing that you were not redeemed with corruptible things, like silver or gold, from your aimless conduct received by tradition from your fathers, but with the precious blood of Christ, as of a lamb without blemish and without spot.*"

      _____

   c) Romans 3:25 - "*Whom God set forth as a propitiation by his blood, through faith, to demonstrate His righteousness, because in His forbearance God had passed over the sins that were previously committed....*" _____

   d) John 1:29 - "*The next day John saw Jesus coming toward him, and said, 'Behold! The Lamb of God who takes away the sin of the world!'*" _____

   e) John 6:53 - "*Then Jesus said to them, 'Most assuredly, I say to you, unless you eat the flesh of the Son of Man and drink His blood, you have no life in you.'*" _____

f) John 12:1,12,13 - *"Then, six days before the Passover, Jesus came to Bethany....The next day a great multitude that had come to the feast, when they heard that Jesus was coming to Jerusalem, took branches of palm trees and went out to meet Him, and cried out: 'Hosanna! Blessed is He who comes in the name of the Lord! The King of Israel!'"* (Hint: Like the Passover lamb, He came to Jerusalem in time to be carefully examined by the leaders before Passover Day.) _____

g) John 19:33 - *"But when they came to Jesus and saw that He was already dead, they did not break His legs."* _____

MEMORY: EXODUS 12:14

Day Four: Exodus 12, continued

1. In Exodus 12:12-13 we have two phrases: *"I will pass through"* and *"I will pass over."* Explain what these meant to the Egyptians and the Israelites. _____

_____

2. The deliverance out of Egypt was so important that God told them to change the calendar to emphasize it. Write down the verse from Exodus 12 that tells about this. _____

3. a) God's instruction was that future generations were to be taught the meaning of the Passover. Who was to do the teaching? _____

b) Do you think God expects the same from parents today as far as the spiritual training of children is concerned? _____

_____

_____

Day Five: The Exodus

Match the following:

_____1. called for Moses and Aaron by night, and said, *"Rise,...serve the Lord... and bless me also"*

_____2. urged the people to leave in haste or *"We shall all be dead"*

_____3. left so quickly, this didn't rise

_____4. what they asked the Egyptians to give them

_____5. number of men leaving

_____6. how long they had been in Egypt

    a) 600,000   d) 430 years

    b) bread   e) Pharaoh

    c) silver, gold, and clothing   f) Egyptians

7. Now take a few minutes to read your study notes for this lesson.

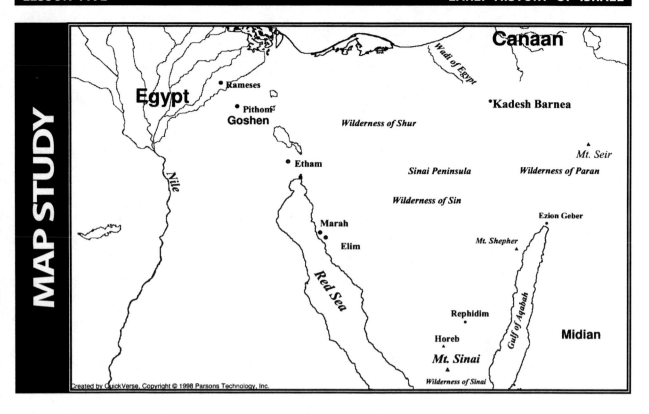

Please refer to this map as you study the Exodus of God's people in the following chapters.

Notes

The Passover and Exodus

The Passover
Exodus 12

God wanted us to understand His plan for us. He is such a master-teacher that He not only explained His great truths in words but also illustrated them with powerful word-pictures. Here in the description of the Passover, we have the scene painted for us so effectively that we can sense the anxiety of Israel's hurried preparation, feel the warmth of the slain lamb's blood, long for a taste of the roasted meat, and hear the joyful sighs of slaves set free.

A New
Beginning

In Exodus 12:2, the importance of the Passover event to the future of Israel was declared by God as He ordered a change in the way the calendar was to be kept. From then on, the month of Passover (Abib or Nisan) would be the first month of their **ecclesiastical** calendar instead of the seventh as it had been. Later the Jews had two calendars. This ecclesiastical one scheduled the observances of the festivals God required while the **civil** one preserved the original order of the months for buying, selling, and non-religious affairs.

> **ecclesiastical** - of or relating to a church or religious body

> **civil** - of or relating to the state or its citizens

lintel - horizontal support above a door opening

Just as the way of our salvation has been provided by the sacrifice of Jesus for us on the cross, we must by faith personally apply His blood to our spiritual houses or bodies if we want to be saved.

atoning - reconciling; satisfying a demand

Following Directions

Beginning with Exodus 12:3, God gave very specific instructions for what people should do if they wanted to be spared from the tenth plague of death to the firstborn. Careful obedience would bring them safety, while any disobedience would bring them death. God had provided a way of escape, but they had to receive the protection by obeying His direction. To kill the lamb and then say, "Well, it won't make any difference whether I put the blood on the door post and the **lintel**—God will understand," would have been partial obedience, unacceptable to God. Just as the way of our salvation has been provided by the sacrifice of Jesus for us on the cross, we must by faith personally apply His blood to our spiritual houses or bodies if we want to be saved. The blood of Christ's sacrifice does not help us until we personally confess Him to be our Savior and believe that His blood is covering our sins. We must acknowledge Him as our own Lamb of God, who takes away sin.

The Power of the Blood

"When I see the blood, I will pass over you" (Exodus 12:13). An essential truth is given in the direction for applying the blood to the doorposts and lintel of each home. Later on the law from Mount Sinai would cry out, *"Whoever has sinned against Me, I will blot him out of My book"* (Exodus 32:33). From this death sentence we, through the **atoning** work of Christ on the cross, are spared. We can only be made alive to God through the shed blood of the Lamb and its application, as required by God through His Word, to our hearts by faith. This is the central idea of all God's revelations to us. In it we find hope of divine favor, all strength to resist and conquer sin, and all power to live a holy life.

Emphasized in Scripture

The power of the blood is awesome! If you are redeemed it is because *"we have redemption through His blood"* (Colossians 1:14). If you are ransomed from sin, it is not that you are ransomed with corruptible things such as silver and gold, *"but with the precious blood of Christ, as of a lamb without blemish and without spot"* (1 Peter 1:18-19). If you are justified, it is because you are *"justified by His blood"* (Romans 5:9). If you are cleansed and made holy, it is because *"the blood of Jesus Christ...cleanses...from all sin"* (1 John 1:7). If you wander from God and need restoration, *"...you who once were far off have been brought near by the blood of Christ"* (Ephesians 2:13). You have access to the Father through prayer because Jesus Christ is our High Priest. Dressed in spotless robes to appear before the Great King are those who *"washed their robes and made them white in the blood of the Lamb"* (Revelation 7:14). If sinners are cast out to eternal death, it is because they chose to trample *"the Son of God underfoot, counted the blood of the covenant by which he was sanctified a common thing, and insulted the Spirit of grace"* (Hebrews 10:29).

All mercy, compassion and grace of God has its foundation in the blood: *"Now the blood shall be a sign for you on the houses where you are. And when I see the blood, I will pass over you; and the plague shall not be on you to destroy you when I strike the land of Egypt"* (Exodus 12:13).

All mercy, compassion and grace of God has its foundation in the blood.

Regularly Remembered
Exodus 12:14-20

The Passover was so important that God ordered it to be re-enacted with a special celebration every year. In fact, it was at an annual Passover observance that Jesus ate the "last supper" with His disciples in an upper room in Jerusalem. During that Passover meal, Jesus compared His coming crucifixion to the sacrifice of the Passover lamb and told them to remember regularly His body and blood when they had that meal together. Our Lord's Supper (Holy Communion) comes from the original Passover, and so when we participate in it, we are celebrating our own deliverance from the bondage of sin as well as remembering what Christ did to make it possible (Matthew 26:28).

The First One

Moses, having received his instructions from the Lord as to the observance of the Passover feast, called for the elders of Israel and communicated to them the divine directions. Probably due to the hatred and jealousy of Pharaoh, a general assembly of the people could not be called. The elders would communicate to the heads of the families, and the whole congregation would know what God required to bring about their deliverance.

Parents as Teachers
Exodus 12:26-27

Spiritual instruction is an essential part of a child's life. In our day when the truth of God's Word is so often distorted or denied, parents must know the meaning and significance of this important teaching of the Passover to be able to present it to their children. Do we set such an example before our family, friends, and peers that they ask us to explain to them the meaning of following Christ?

Time's Up!
Exodus 12:27-30

"So the people bowed their heads and worshiped. Then the children of Israel went away and did so; just as the Lord had commanded Moses and Aaron, so they did." While Israel sat within their homes with the blood of the lamb on their doorways, God Himself loosed the tenth plague. Like a wave, a wail of anguish passed from Egyptian home to Egyptian home. Without the blood, none were exempt; from the pasture to the palace, the first-born died.

At last the heart of Pharaoh was broken. He yielded because he could no longer resist.

At last the heart of Pharaoh was broken. He was touched by the terrible tenth plague to the point of not only granting the Israelites all their demands but also asking them for their blessing. He yielded because he could no longer resist. The Egyptians shared the feelings of their king. They gave the Israelites all they asked for in jewels, silver, gold, and clothing. They were anxious to get rid of these neighbors at any price.

Israel had been in slavery for many years; now they left the land with the well-earned reward for their long labor and intense sorrow. One day in the future they would need these valuables to answer Moses' request for materials to build a place of worship in the wilderness. If these details had not been recorded, we would have thought such a request from long-time slaves impossible to fulfill.

Israel had been in slavery for many years; now they left the land with the well-earned reward for their long labor and intense sorrow.

Out of There!
Exodus 12:37-51

The facts of the actual exodus of the children of Israel were recorded briefly. God had saved "six hundred thousand men" in spite of Pharaoh's cruelty. When the number of women, children, and "mixed multitude" were figured in to this, perhaps as many as two million people moved out of the land in one day with the flocks and herds. It was indeed a great night, a great deliverance. It served as a picture and a prophecy of the complete escape each believer would be provided through the blood of Jesus Christ.

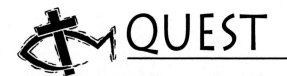 QUEST

Questions

Study Procedure: Read the Scripture references before answering questions. Unless otherwise instructed, use the Bible only in answering questions. Some questions may be more difficult than others but try to answer as many as you can. Pray for God's wisdom and understanding as you study and don't be discouraged if some answers are not obvious at first. Do not read the study notes for this lesson until AFTER you have completed your questions.

Day One:

1. Vocabulary Review: From your notes, define the following:

   a) atoning _____

   b) civil _____

   c) lintel _____

   d) ecclesiastical _____

2. If you were teaching a lesson on the Passover, what would you want to emphasize and why? (Exodus 12) _____

   _____

   _____

   _____

3. From last week's lesson, compare briefly the first Passover with the last days and crucifixion of Jesus. _____

   _____

   _____

   _____

   _____

   _____

MEMORY: EXODUS 13:21-22

Day Two: Read Exodus 13

1. Consider what Moses faced in moving as many as two million people from one place to another.

   a) List some of the concerns that would have to be addressed. _____

   _____

   _____

   b) How could Moses handle these? _____

   _____

2. After their miraculous escape, to whom did the first-born of the Israelites belong? Give verse.

   _____

3. Who previously claimed the Israelites as slaves? _____

4. List any reasons you can think of as to why God did not allow Israel to go directly to the land of

   Canaan? _____

   _____

   _____

5. From Exodus 13:21-22, describe God's unique protection of Israel. _____

   _____

   _____

Day Three: Read Exodus 14   MEMORY: EXODUS 14:13-14

1. From a Bible atlas or the maps in your Bible, locate the route of the exodus and the years in the

   wilderness. Study their escape route out of Egypt.

2. God had told the Israelites they were going to the land of Canaan (Exodus 13:5). What is strange

   about the directions He gave Moses to follow? _____

   _____

3. At the departure of the children of Israel, of what losses would the Egyptians soon become aware?

   _____

   _____

4. What action did Pharaoh take when he learned the direction the Hebrews took? _____

   _____

Day Four: Continue reading Chapter 14

1. With Pharaoh in pursuit, mountains on one side and the sea on the other, how do you think the

   Israelites were feeling? _____

   _____

2. Review the verses in the first part of Exodus 14 in which God prepared them for this turn of

   events.

   a) Should they have given in to their fears? Explain. _____

   _____

   _____

b) Do you have a similar personal experience to share here? _____

_____

_____

3. a) To whom were the children of Israel forced to turn? (Give verse.) _____

   b) Whom did they turn against? _____

   c) What do you think they referred to when they said there were no graves in Egypt? (Exodus 11)

_____

_____

4. Write down the two commands found in the references below and who issued them.

   a) Exodus 14:13 - _____

   b) Exodus 14:15 - _____

MEMORY: PSALM 103:11-14

Day Five: Continue reading Chapter 14 and 15; Psalm 103

1. **Thought Question:** What is your behavior under pressure? Do you first of all pray, then step out in courage and faith to do what God wants you to do? _____

_____

_____

_____

2. List the many specific ways God protected and delivered Israel in Exodus 14. _____

_____

_____

_____

_____

_____

3. Read the wonderful song of praise in Exodus 15. They praised God very specifically for who He was and what He did. List several of these specific praises. _____

_____

_____

_____

4. What did the song declare would be the result of such a miraculous deliverance? (verses 14-18)

_____

_____

5. Now take a few minutes to read your study notes for this lesson.

Notes

Out of Egypt and Across the Sea

God Claims Firstborn
Exodus 13:1-6

consecrate - to devote to a specific purpose

Without God's protection, the firstborn of Israel would have been killed like the firstborn of Egypt. They were protected by the blood of the sacrificial Passover lamb, ,and, in the first verses of Exodus 13, God claimed them as His own. "*Consecrate to Me all the firstborn...it is Mine.*" When something was consecrated, it was set apart for a specific use. Paul says in 1 Corinthians 6:19-20, "*Or do you not know that...you are not your own? For you were bought at a price; therefore glorify God in your body and in your spirit, which are God's.*" The firstborn of man was saved to serve, set apart for holy service to God. The firstborn of the animals was offered to God in sacrifice and worship.

Consecration Requires Separation from Evil

leaven - yeast

permeates - spreads or diffuses throughout

Moses, in his instructions for the consecration of the firstborn, repeated the requirements for the Feast of Unleavened Bread, which was an additional seven-day period surrounding Passover that God directed to be set aside each year. Generally, **leaven** or yeast in Scripture, is a symbol of corruption, because it **permeates** a substance to cause expansion or "rising." To partake of the Passover, the Israelites had to remove all leaven from the home. This was another word-picture for us to illustrate the truth that we, too, should be careful to remove all evil from our lives as we daily serve God. If we have been redeemed by the blood of Christ, we belong to Him. Our service requires a holy life. We do not serve Christ to be saved, but we serve Him because we are saved. Conversion to Jesus Christ is followed by consecration, and this demands purity and holiness of living (Romans 12).

We do not serve Christ to be saved, but we serve Him because we are saved.

Consecration Requires Education

To be set apart to serve God involved a process of study and teaching. All parents were responsible for instructing their children about the meaning of the great deliverance from Egypt, the significance of the consecration, and the purpose of the Feast of Unleavened Bread. Is it not as vital today for Christians to teach others the meaning of salvation and consecration and what this involves in their commitment to Christ our Redeemer?

God's Word has the answer to every problem. Let us know it through prayerful study so as God gives us opportunity, we may properly guide others in the truth of God's Word.

Goshen to the Red Sea
Exodus 13:17-22

When the Israelites occupied the land in Egypt, the term "Goshen" belonged to a region which had no definite boundaries, extending with the increase of people over the territory. "Land of the Rameses" applied to a larger area, and Rameses and Succoth were names of districts as well as cities. The distance between these places was not necessarily a single day's journey. It is possible that nearly three weeks had elapsed between the night of the Passover in Goshen-Rameses and the night at the Red Sea.

Each Israelite family, after receiving gifts from its Egyptian neighbors, turned its steps toward the border. Israel moved without any fear of the Egyptians, who were busy burying their dead. It probably took several days for the gathering of the children of Israel at Succoth after their hurried exodus.

In order to avoid getting involved in the on-going wars of the Philistines, God instructed Moses to take a route more difficult *"by way of the wilderness of the Red Sea."* The spirits of the Israelites were broken with slavery, and the Philistines were too fierce an enemy for them to encounter at this time. Then, too, God needed to prepare them for the wars of Canaan through their experiences in the wilderness journeys. Every stage of the journey contained something instructive.

Every stage of the journey contained something instructive.

Encouragement from the Past
Exodus 13:19

Four hundred years before the exit from Egypt, Israel had entered that country in order to escape famine. One of their own **kinsmen**, Joseph, had been blessed by God and raised to power. Yet, nothing in Joseph's lifetime was quite as significant as the directions he left at his death. He so loved his people and had such an unswerving faith in God that he wanted his very bones to encourage Israel's faith and to glorify God. Joseph believed God would visit His people and lead them out of Egypt, but he knew that their faith might fail if the waiting was long. Nothing he could say or do in his lifetime would have had as much meaning to the people as this last request that his bones be left unburied until they could be buried in Canaan, when God fulfilled his promise to Abraham and took them back. As they bore the coffin in the wilderness, they would remember their destination and be encouraged in their faith and patience. The coffin was a silent pledge that their wanderings would certainly cease and that they would, indeed, rest in the land promised to their fathers.

kinsmen - relatives

Powerful Pillar
Exodus 13:20-22

The **pillar** of cloud by day and fire by night was the symbol of God's presence with His people. This was His "Shekinah" or "visible glory." God used this means to guide and protect His people as they camped or journeyed.

pillar - a column or shaft standing alone

Today we have as our guide the Word of God, which is a lamp to our feet and a light to our path (Psalms 119:105). We have the Holy Spirit to reveal His truth and direct us on our journey. The Israelites were not to look on the road they were travelling as to its smoothness or roughness; they were only to follow the cloud and follow wherever it led them. Even so, we too are responsible to obey God's Word in walking through life. How important it is to know how to read and follow God's map and guidebook as we travel! We have the brightness of the Father's glory, God appearing in the flesh, our Lord and Saviour Jesus Christ, with us.

A Trap or a Test?
Exodus 14:1-29

The march of the Israelites was through Succoth to Etham, then to Baal-Zephon, and then to the place of crossing the Red Sea. It was between the sea and mountain range that the children of Israel awaited God's guidance for crossing the sea. Pharaoh, hearing about the Israelites, thought they had mistakenly taken the wrong way and were now trapped. He was sure their fate was in his control and decided to pursue them. Pharaoh was still fighting against God. He called together 600 war chariots and his men of war; they headed toward the sea.

"Do not be afraid." Moses told the frightened people, "Stand still, and see the salvation of the Lord, which He will accomplish for you today."

Israel saw in a distance the rapid advance of Pharaoh and his force of chariots. Is it any wonder that they lost heart? Moses alone kept his head and his faith. There seemed to be no way of escape, but his faith expected deliverance from Jehovah. *"Do not be afraid."* Moses told the frightened people, *"Stand still, and see the salvation of the Lord, which He will accomplish for you today."* What a lesson for the church to learn today! The church's spiritual success is *"'not by might nor by power, but by My Spirit,' says the Lord of hosts"* (Zechariah 4:6). Let us take courage and pray, believing God, then move ahead as God instructed Moses to do. There is no time to nurse horror and fear; the command is, *"Go forward."* Refuse to let doubt fill your thoughts. Choose to take the next necessary step; faith is doing right even when the feelings are absent. Soon enough all will see the salvation of God!

presumption - a belief dictated by a probability

In contrast to the obedience of Israel, Pharaoh's army followed without God's approval. There is no protection from God promised when we venture selfishly or foolishly into danger. Pharaoh tried to cross the sea, and he was drowned. The Hebrews, following their God, went over on dry land. Faith is one thing; **presumption** is another. To go recklessly into danger is presumption; to go through that danger in His service is courage. For Israel, God made the impossible possible and caused the sea to be divided. For Egypt, He caused the waters to join together. The very thing the Israelites feared would destroy them was used to protect them. This miracle was caused by God's power. This description of the crossing of the Red Sea needs little comment, and it was the greatest miracle in the history of mankind since the Genesis flood.

No Mud Between Their Toes!

When God asks His children to do something, He provides sufficiently for their success. God ordered the wind to dry the ground for their safe crossing; no detail was too small for Him to notice. He also perfectly timed the return of the waters so as to use even the re-formed mud to stall the chariot wheels of Egypt. God will judge those who try to harm His people. The Egyptian corpses on the banks of the Red Sea assured the children of Israel of that great truth.

When God asks His children to do something, He provides sufficiently for their success.

A Pause for Praise
Exodus 15:1-21

Overwhelmed by God's miraculous deliverance from certain death and the overthrow of Pharaoh's 600 chariots, the children of Israel were led by **Miriam** and others in a grand song of celebration. No tired or **trite** phrases of praise here, but very specific thanksgiving to God for particular actions. In verses 1-12 the song focused on the miracle at the Red Sea: *"I will sing to the Lord, for He has triumphed gloriously! The horse and its rider He has thrown into the sea!"* (verse 1). *"The enemy said, 'I will pursue, I will overtake,'...You blew with Your wind, the sea covered them; they sank like lead in the mighty waters"* (verses 9,10). The second half looked forward to the Lord's help in the future: *"The people will hear and be afraid; sorrow will take hold of the **inhabitants** of Philistia"* (verse 14). *"...by the greatness of Your arm they will be as still as a stone, till Your people pass over, O Lord,...You will bring them in and plant them in the mountain of Your inheritance,..."* (verses 16,17). This Song of Redemption has reached down through the centuries and is the oldest song in the Bible. Even today, our deepest spiritual experiences are effectively expressed through godly music.

Miriam - older sister of Moses

trite - overused; stale

inhabitants - permanent residents

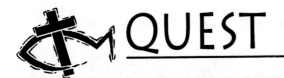

Questions

Study Procedure: Read the Scripture references before answering questions. Unless otherwise instructed, use the Bible only in answering questions. Some questions may be more difficult than others but try to answer as many as you can. Pray for God's wisdom and understanding as you study and don't be discouraged if some answers are not obvious at first. Do not read the study notes for this lesson until AFTER you have completed your questions.

MEMORY: ZECHARIAH 4:6

Day One: Vocabulary: Matching

_____1. consecrate	a)	spreads or diffuses throughout
_____2. inhabitants	b)	overused; stale
_____3. kinsmen	c)	yeast
_____4. leaven	d)	to devote to a specific purpose
_____5. Miriam	e)	permanent residents
_____6. permeates	f)	a column or shaft standing alone
_____7. pillar	g)	older sister of Moses
_____8. presumption	h)	relatives
_____9. trite	i)	a belief dictated by a probability

10. Summarize from last week's notes what it means to be consecrated to God. _____

_____

_____

_____

MEMORY: EXODUS 15:2, 26

Day Two: Read Exodus 15:22-27; Exodus 16-17

1. In Chapters 15-17 the children of Israel make four important stops. As you read through these chapters, note below what you find meaningful or surprising about each one. Also note the nature of their "test" at each stop, where one is mentioned.

a) Marah _____

_____

Reference: _____

b) Elim _____

_____

Reference: _____

c) Wilderness of Sin _____

_____

Reference: _____

d) Rephidim _____

_____

_____ Reference: _____

2. With a pen trace the above places on your map.

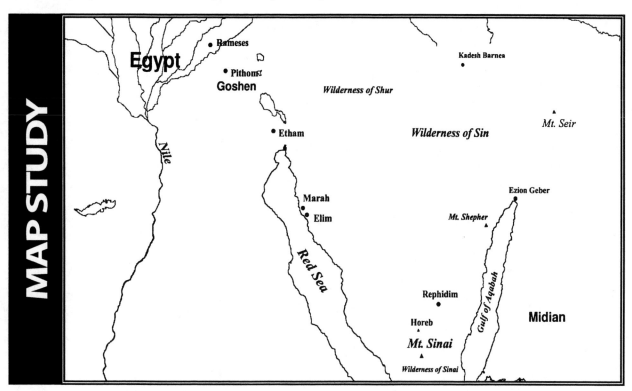

MAP STUDY

MEMORY: PSALM 104:33

Day Three:

1. Contrasting the words and actions surrounding the wonderful song of praise recorded in Exodus
   15 with the attitude of the children of Israel as they encountered problems in these chapters,
   what misconceived idea could they have had about their new life with God?

   _____

2. Do you feel there is a parallel of this when a person becomes a Christian? _____

   _____

   _____

   _____

3. Reread the wonderful promise God gave them in 15:26. Break it down under the headings below.
   "If you... _____

   _____

"I will... _____

_____

"For I am... _____

_____

Day Four: Match these phrases with the correct passages:

_____1. Those were the good old days.   a) Exodus 17:10-13

_____2. Feed the need, not the greed.   b) Exodus 17:14-16

_____3. Popularity is a fragile thing.   c) Exodus 16:3

_____4. Spiritual warfare is hard, too.   d) Exodus 17:7

_____5. When God has something recorded, it's serious!   e) Exodus 16:16-21

_____6. I can't believe they said that!   f) Exodus 17:4

_____7. Too much of a good thing?   g) Exodus 16:35

_____8. Our first look at this future leader.   h) Exodus 17:9

Day Five: Read Chapter 18. This is an "up close and personal" passage about Moses and his family. Summarize what you find out about each of the following topics.

1. Jethro (verses 1-12)

   a) his relationship with Moses _____

   _____

   b) his relationship to God _____

   _____

2. Moses (verses 13-27)

   a) his workload _____

   _____

   b) his ability to listen to advice _____

   _____

   c) his relief _____

   _____

3. Now take a few minutes to read your study notes for this lesson.

Notes

Off to a Rough Start

Murmuring at Marah
Exodus 15:22-23

With confidence high after the miraculous display of God's power at the Red Sea, Israel followed their leader across the unfamiliar wilderness. Troubled with thirst because of the hot desert climate, they wanted water. However, after finding bitter water at Marah, their first encampment, they murmured against Moses. What a beginning for their journey to the land of promise—thirst and bitterness! God had so miraculously brought them through the Red Sea that they perhaps thought the future days would be trouble-free.

With confidence high after the miraculous display of God's power at the Red Sea, Israel followed their leader across the unfamiliar wilderness.

We, too, are often surprised when troubles come to us. Why would God allow us to be uncomfortable? Like Israel, we need to get rid of our slave-mentality. They had spent years just reacting to their circumstances, whether harsh or mild, instead of seeking ways to change them. As free people under God's authority, they were to stop being so short-sighted and self-centered and begin to allow God at all times to let them see things as He sees them. As individuals, they had to learn to think first about what would honor God and quit being moved by herd instincts. Their thirst problem was certainly not difficult for the God who just manipulated the Red Sea for His purposes. They were to trust God, pray for His help or direction, but certainly not murmur against their leader. Fortunately, Moses was far ahead of them in spiritual maturity since his own graduation from the desert, and he turned to God, whom he knew as his only source of help.

Wood in the Water
Exodus 15:24-25

God answered by showing Moses a tree that could be cast into the waters to sweeten them. For us today, there is still a tree, a tree on Calvary, which held the very Son of God, who is more than able to remove the bitterness of sin, deprivation, and sickness from our lives.

statutes - regulations

Early Orders
Exodus 15:26

While the stop at Marah was God's test to expose the weaknesses of Israel, it was also His chosen place to give them the first of many clear **statutes** or **ordinances** regarding their behavior. They were free from Egypt now, brought into His own protecting love, and their behavior should reflect their new situation. This statute was simple: if they would listen and obey, He would keep them from the sicknesses they had seen in the plagues on Egypt. He declared Himself to be the *"Lord who heals you."* Like children of a famous father, they would only gradually discover that their father had more talents than just what he had

ordinances - orders; something decreed

displayed in their living room. Their next encampments would bring more tests and more teachings.

Easier at Elim
Exodus 15:27

"Then they came to Elim, where there were twelve wells of water and seventy palm trees; so they camped there by the waters." Shade and water are two of the most comforting provisions in the desert. The life of the child of God is not all hardship and testing. This was truly an **oasis** for them, but it **was** not their destination. They had to move on.

oasis - something providing relief from the usual

The Name Says It All: Wilderness of Sin
Exodus 16

God was disciplining them and training them to exercise faith in Him. Hunger now threatened the children of Israel, and under this fear they seemed to forget the miracles of the past. Their faith was really being tested. We have a picture here of the human heart—God had brought them out of slavery, yet they wanted to go back to Pharaoh and become slaves again. How could they so soon forget the bitterness of their life in bondage? How could they so soon forget the blessings of their new life of trusting and following God?

Manna in the Morning
Exodus 16:4-36

God heard the murmurings of the children of Israel and promised them help. He would give bread from heaven which they would have to gather every day to eat. God made the gathering of their daily **ration** a test of their willingness to simply hear, believe, and obey. Many failed the test. Some tried to hoard extra portions, but the extra *"bred worms and stank."* Moses was angry (verse 20). Some went out looking for manna on the Sabbath, dishonoring the day of rest, instead of gathering double the day before. When they ignored God's **stipulations**, they found none.

ration - portion; share

stipulations - specific requirements

Been There, Done That

What Israel demonstrated here was that disobedience is basically unbelief. When we really believe that God is God and that, once we are in His family, He will care for all our needs, then we have no need to disobey. Scheming, **hoarding**, or trying to get ahead of someone else will not be necessary because we are sure that God will take care of His own. However, when we disobey, we are showing that we really do not believe that God has told us the truth or that He is able and willing to take care of our every need. We, like Israel of old, do not obey because we do not believe.

hoarding - gathering and hiding a supply

New Testament Application

For forty years God fed Israel in the wilderness. No other generation in the course of human history had been cared for in such a way. In the New Testament, Jesus referred to this section of Scripture and told His listeners that the manna their fathers ate in the wilderness for forty years was not given them by Moses, but by God to meet their physical needs. Jesus meets more than our physical needs. He said of Himself, *"I am the bread of life. He who comes to Me shall never hunger, and he who believes in Me shall never thirst"* (John 6:35). Our spiritual hunger and thirst today are met in the Person of Jesus Christ. Jesus taught us to pray, *"Give us this day our daily bread,"* and so we are regularly to spend time in prayer and study, gathering enough "manna" for each day. On Sunday, we are not to gather for ourselves but go to a place of worship and have our "meal," which has been prepared ahead of time, with others.

Our spiritual hunger and thirst today are met in the Person of Jesus Christ.

Repetition at Rephidim
Exodus 17:1-7

"According to the commandment of the Lord," Israel left the Wilderness of Sin and camped at Rephidim. They went where God led; yet there was no water in that place. God was allowing a "make-up test" here, but they did not realize it. As usual, their first response was to demand from Moses what they needed: *"Give us water, that we may drink."* When would they learn to quit looking at every situation from only their own view and choose to consider what God might be doing in it? God had led them there; surely He had a plan for giving them water. Instead of "tempting God" to punish them with their murmuring, they should have prayed and waited to see His power once again. God does not lead where He does not intend to provide. Their murmuring was so serious that Moses felt a threat upon his life. He prayed to the Lord and was directed to go to Horeb with his shepherd's staff, taking the elders to witness the miracle. Horeb was perhaps the last place Moses would have gone for water. He might have expected that **smiting** the rock would have brought forth fire rather than refreshing water.

smiting - striking sharply or heavily

Warfare on Two Levels
Exodus 17:8-16

The second important event at Rephidim was the battle with Amalek. It seemed the children of Israel were alone in the desert, but at this point an enemy came against them: a nomadic tribe, descendants of Esau, who were inhabiting the region southeast of the Dead Sea. A victory over such a **foe** was of great importance to the Hebrew people, as the Amalekites were one of the greatest peoples of this remote region. The reason for the attack is not given. It must have been a ruthless and cowardly attack coming in the midst of the miracle at the rock. They attacked from behind, and this probably involved the weary and weak Israelites who had not caught up with the camp (Deuteronomy 25:17-18). Because of their disregard for God and His people, the Lord said to Moses, *"I will utterly blot out the remembrance of Amalek from under heaven"* (verse 14). This sentence was carried out partly by King Saul (1 Samuel 15) and completed by King David (1 Samuel 30; 2 Samuel 1:1-8, 12).

foe - enemy

New Leader Introduced

Joshua, the future leader of the children of Israel, is mentioned here for the first time. Moses chose Joshua to lead the battle against the Amalekites. The physical battle was in the valley, but there was a spiritual battle on the mountain above. Moses took Aaron and Hur there where Moses held up the rod of God in view of the battle. As long as he held it up, there was victory below. When Moses tired, Aaron and Hur supported him. This speaks to us of the importance of supportive prayer and of winning victory over the enemy who would seek to defeat us in our walk and work for God. *"Jehovah-nissi, The-Lord-Is-My-Banner,"* was their grateful acknowledgment that they had gone into battle, not under their own "flag" of power, but under the banner or authority of God Himself. When they defeated the enemy, God received all the credit. We have physical success where there has been spiritual victory from God in answer to prayer.

The physical battle was in the valley, but there was a spiritual battle on the mountain above.

Good Advice
Exodus 18:1-27

This is the third event which occurred at Rephidim and is important because of the appointing of rulers to help Moses in his work with the people. The children of Israel were near the home of Moses' father-in-law, Jethro. Jethro brought to Moses his wife and two children, who no doubt had been with Jethro in Midian for the past months. Observing that Moses had great responsibility in judging the people, Jethro gave Moses advice about delegating authority to others to lighten his load. Moses accepted his advice; after which Jethro returned to his own land.

Important Stop
Exodus 19:1

After about a six-weeks' journey, Israel reached Sinai in the third month. They had traveled about 200 miles and would stay here almost a year. It was at this place that God would give Israel a renewed covenant and calling and would begin the task of organizing Israel as a nation.

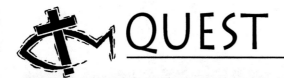
Questions

Study Procedure: Read the Scripture references before answering questions. Unless otherwise instructed, use the Bible only in answering questions. Some questions may be more difficult than others but try to answer as many as you can. Pray for God's wisdom and understanding as you study and don't be discouraged if some answers are not obvious at first. Do not read the study notes for this lesson until AFTER you have completed your questions.

Day One: Vocabulary Matching

MEMORY: JOHN 6:35

_____1. stipulations

_____2. hoarding

_____3. ration

_____4. oasis

_____5. foe

_____6. statutes

_____7. ordinances

_____8. smiting

a) regulations

b) orders; something decreed

c) something providing relief from the usual

d) portion; share

e) specific requirements

f) gathering and hiding a supply

g) striking sharply or heavily

h) enemy

9. Matching:

_____a) the place where the children of Israel complained because they didn't have water

_____b) the place where they found undrinkable water

_____c) the place where they complained about having no food

_____d) Moses' father-in-law

_____e) an oasis in the the desert

_____f) Israel's enemy

1. Rephidim   2. Jethro   3. Amalek   4. Wilderness of Sin   5. Marah   6. Elim

10. Give a description of the bread from heaven called manna. Write down anything especially interesting, helpful, or encouraging from last week's notes that had to do with manna.

_____

_____

_____

_____

_____

Day Two: Read Exodus, Chapters 19 and 20

1. Using Exodus 19:1-7, write down the expressive terms God used to describe the plans He had for Israel if they would obey His voice and keep His covenant.

   a) _____

   b) _____

   c) _____

2. What had He already done for them? _____

_____

3. Do you think the children of Israel understood their own weaknesses and tendency to sin when they so quickly agreed to the conditions of obedience? _____

_____

_____

4. Give a description of the morning when the Lord came down to talk to Israel. _____

_____

_____

_____

Day Three:

MEMORY: MATTHEW 22:36-40

1. a) List the verses in Exodus 19 containing warnings against any unholy curiosity in approaching the mountain from which God was to speak. _____

   _____

   b) Is there something that we can learn here about our attitude or actions in relation to approaching God? _____

   _____

2. Jesus was asked a question by the Pharisees: *"Teacher, which is the greatest commandment in the law?"* (Matthew 22:36). Jesus responded with two new commandments, which in essence included all ten of the commandments.

   a) *"Love the Lord your God with all your heart, with all your soul, and with all your mind."* List from Exodus 20 the commandments that could be categorized under this summary.

   _____

   _____

   _____

   _____

b) *"Love your neighbor as yourself."* List from Exodus 20 the commandments that could be summarized with this one. _____

_____

_____

_____

_____

3. Why do you think the commandments are addressed in the singular? _____

_____

4. In Exodus 20:23, the Lord emphasizes one particular commandment as to idols. Why do you think He needed to do this to a new nation so recently removed from Egypt? _____

_____

_____

Day Four: Read Exodus 21-23

Note: The Ten Commandments are God's law, given in outline in Exodus 20. In Exodus 21-23, the law is given in detail. In Exodus 20 God lays down the great eternal principles, and in Chapters 21-23 He gives certain applications of these principles to everyday life.

1. From Exodus 21-23, list some of the details of daily life in which, according to the laws given in these chapters, God is interested. _____

_____

_____

_____

2. What does God reveal about human nature in each of these chapters?

   a) Chapter 21 _____

   _____

   b) Chapter 22 _____

   c) Chapter 23 _____

3. What word is found in Exodus 22 that is frequently neglected today even in the Christian life?

   _____

4. In Exodus 23:20-33, God gave both promises and warnings to the children of Israel. List the promises found in the following verses.

   a) verses 20-22 _____

   _____

   b) verses 23-30 _____

   _____

   c) verse 31 _____

Day Five: Read Exodus 24

1. Covenant-making involved at least two parties pledging benefits or services to each other. This 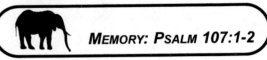 **MEMORY: PSALM 107:1-2**
was taken very seriously and only entered into after clear explanation of terms and much consideration of the cost of upholding it. Once sealed, traditionally with blood, the covenant could not be broken except by death: natural death ended it or execution of the party failing to meet the agreement ended it. Some common elements such as changes or additions to covenant-partners' names (like a woman taking her husband's last name in marriage), exchange of weaponry, clothing, or property are not seen in this chapter. However, several common covenant actions are described.

Note the verses that correspond with the following:

a) Chosen representative(s) for the group or partners entering a covenant _____

b) Clearly communicated and recorded terms of covenant _____

c) Witnesses_____

d) Sealing of covenant with blood _____

e) Eating a meal together _____

f) Giving of gift or token to memorialize the covenant _____

2. In Exodus 24:12, what did God tell Moses was the purpose of the tablets? _____

_____

3. a) Who went up with Moses to the mountain? _____

b) Who stayed behind? _____

c) Why? _____

4. According to verse 18, how long did the meeting last? _____

5. Now take a few minutes to read your study notes for this lesson.

Notes

Mt. Sinai—the Covenant and the Law

No Guessing: Covenant Love Explained

covenant - formal, solemn, and binding agreement

Our Creator God loved man so much that He wanted him not only to be joined together with Him in an official union or **covenant**, but also to enter that union willingly, based on a personal knowledge of who He is and an awareness of what a relationship with Him would require. However, man could never have known Him if He had not communicated with him directly and then had that communication recorded for future generations in the Scriptures.

Think About It Do we realize how special the Word of God is? Without it, we could only guess about the nature of God, filling in the huge gaps of knowledge that exist with bits of information from our observation of the magnificent orderliness of the universe. Without the clear word of Scripture we would never be sure if we had obeyed correctly or if God had only good intentions toward us.

Nothing New Here in these chapters, God communicated in clear terms what He would do for Israel and what He expected Israel to do in response to their relationship with Him. The covenant or contract that would bind Israel to God and God to Israel had some conditions—conditions of obedience. Chapters 19-24 gave the terms of what was called the Mosaic covenant. Moses was the "middle man" here, receiving from God and then giving that word to the people. Yet, this Mosaic covenant was not the first word from God. God had communicated covenant requirements to Adam, Noah, and the **patriarchs** generations before. In our day, God has spoken to us through the New Covenant, sealed not with the blood of sacrificial animals, but with the blood of Jesus Christ.

> **patriarchs** - men who are founders or fathers of a group

> *In our day, God has spoken to us through the New Covenant, sealed not with the blood of sacrificial animals, but with the blood of Jesus Christ.*

God Keeps His Word
Exodus 19:1-2

God had said to Moses when He first called him to duty in Exodus 3:12, *"When you have brought the people out of Egypt, you shall serve God on this mountain."* Now the children of Israel were camping before that very mountain. It must have been with mixed emotions that Moses approached the mountains of Horeb, remembering his experience of the burning bush and his encounter with God. Called and commissioned, Moses had obeyed the Lord. Little could he have realized all that was involved in that call. He had thrust himself before Pharaoh's **tyranny**. He had been God's instrument to bring the children of Israel from a bondage worse than death. His rod divided the Red Sea, an act which meant deliverance to the Israelites and death to their pursuers. His leadership had been challenged as they journeyed to this place where God would give **explicit** instructions to His people. And through it all, Moses learned that it was an easier task to crush the oppressor than to discipline and educate the oppressed.

> **tyranny** - cruel and oppressive government or control

> **explicit** - fully and clearly expressed

Third Month
Exodus 19:1-2

In Hebrew, the term "in the third month," meant "in the third new moon." To us, that translated "on the first day of the third month" or forty-five days after they had left Egypt. If the day Moses went up to God (verse 3) is added, plus the next day when he returned the people's answer to God (verses 7 and 8), and finally the three days mentioned in verses 10 and 11, there would be fifty days from the Passover to the giving of the Law on Mount Sinai. If these calculations are correct, there is an interesting correlation to a feast celebrated later called the Feast of Pentecost, or the fiftieth day. From the New Testament we learn that it was at the Jewish Feast of Pentecost, *"when the Day of Pentecost had fully come,"* (Acts 2:1) that the Holy Ghost was given to the apostles to enable them to communicate to all men the New Covenant of our Lord Jesus Christ. On that day 3000 were saved, but a loss of 3000 resulted the day the Law was given.

Sinai and Horeb

Some historians use these names interchangeably, but from Scripture it seems that Sinai is one particular mountain. The plain at the foot of this particular mountain is called "Wilderness of Sinai." Horeb seems to be the designation of the region generally, or the group of mountains in that region. There is some difference of opinion as to the exactness of this conclusion, since the names of the mountains and valleys have changed through the years. There is no question, however, of the fact of Mount Sinai being the place where God gave the Ten Commandments.

Moses on the Mountain
Exodus 19:3-25

On the plain in front of Mount Sinai, God, through Moses, reminded the people of the past evidence of His power to deliver and of His present purpose to bless them. The beautiful figure of the eagles' wings illustrated the patient tenderness with which the Lord trained His people for their escape from Egypt and protected them as they journeyed. Then to this is added the promise, *"you shall be a special treasure to Me above all people;...a kingdom of priests and a holy nation."* All the nations of the earth belonged to God because He created them; however, Israel was God's, not only by creation, but by selection. God had chosen them to give knowledge of salvation to all the nations and to provide the human line through which the Redeemer would be born.

God had chosen them to give knowledge of salvation to all the nations and to provide the human line through which the Redeemer would be born.

Obedience Required
Exodus 19:5-6

"If you will indeed obey My voice and keep My covenant." Obedience was the key that unlocked the promises given in the laws of Mt. Sinai. God provided the means of salvation, but Israel had to be willing to accept it. Israel was to be a holy people, dwelling in the light through a covenant relationship to God.

Obedience Promised
Exodus 19:7-8

"All that the Lord has spoken we will do." This was the acceptance of the covenant by the people, with Moses acting as the mediator or go-between in the transaction. At this point, Israel was summoned by God to enter into a solemn national covenant with Him. In its spirit and significance, this covenant did not differ from the covenant made with Abraham some 600 years before.

God promised to be God not to Abraham only, but also to his seed after him. The one was a renewal of the other. After this event at the foot of Mount Sinai, the people moved away with a deep awareness that God had spoken. God said, *"I will be your God,"* and the people responded, *"All that the Lord has spoken we will do."* What an opportunity given to a new nation—receiving their laws from God and benefiting by His protection; God dwelling among them, fighting their battles, preserving their going out and coming in; God glorifying their entire existence! Sad to say, Israel never rose to its high calling. Yet as we look back over Israel's history, no knowledge of their weaknesses and human failure ever stopped God from fulfilling His gracious plan.

Sad to say, Israel never rose to its high calling. Yet as we look back over Israel's history, no knowledge of their weaknesses and human failure ever stopped God from fulfilling His gracious plan.

Glory Displayed
Exodus 19:19-25

God knew that the people needed some evidence that what Moses said really came from God Himself, so God planned to give a display of His power. Two days were set aside for cleansing, and a boundary was set so that neither man nor beast could come near the mountain. Death was promised to any who presumed to come uninvited or unprepared. Then, amid thunderings and lightnings, the quaking of the mountain, and the terror of the people, the Lord descended. Now the people heard the voice of God speaking. God was in charge; Moses was only the instrument through whom God chose to reveal His law to the people. The *Shekinah*, or glory of the Lord, appeared in the sight of all the people to convince them of the reality of their God. (For another interesting description not included here, read Deuteronomy 33:2.)

Shekinah - the shining glory of God

Purpose and Summary of the Giving of the Law

By definition, a law is a rule of conduct or action enforced by a controlling authority. The laws of God stated how man should conduct himself and the consequences that followed if he did not. God's laws revealed that God knew well the personality of man, the tendency toward selfishness and ease. By giving clear standards for behavior, God accomplished several things:

1. **Evil was restrained.** Like a fence, the law held in the full expression of evil actions. A speed limit does not stop all speeding, but once established, it tends to lessen just how much over the limit one will go. With no law, there is no restraint.

2. **A standard was set.** A person would not know how far "off the mark" he had gone if there were no "mark." This is what the apostle Paul had in mind when he said that *"the law was our tutor to bring us to Christ"* (Galatians 3:24). The law showed us God's standard and how far away from that standard we had strayed. Man's conscience must be awakened to a sense of sin before he feels his need for salvation in Christ.

Man's conscience must be awakened to a sense of sin before he feels his need of salvation in Christ.

3. **A substitute was offered.** No man could ever continually keep the law or standards of God, so a penalty had to be paid. The established penalty was the blood of a sacrificial animal. Isaiah 53 expressed it like this, *"All we like sheep have gone astray; we have turned everyone, to his own way; and the Lord has laid on Him the iniquity of us all."* The law showed us our need for a Savior and pictured in the acceptable sacrifices allowed, what that Savior would be like.

In Matthew 22:37-40, Jesus summarized the Ten Commandments with two: *"You shall love the Lord your God with all your heart, with all your soul, and with all your mind,"* and *"You shall love your neighbor as yourself."* Christ's words made clear the unity and the Mosaic authorship of the whole covenant when He said, *"On these two commandments hang all the Law and the Prophets."* Neither Christ nor His apostles quoted any other code nor referred to any other lawgiver besides Moses. (See also Luke 20:37; Acts 7:37.)

Christ's words made clear the unity and the Mosaic authorship of the whole covenant when He said, "On these two commandments hang all the Law and the Prophets."

The law of God provides a clear and sharp distinction between right and wrong. Today so often even the Christian is half-hearted about what God calls sin. We need reminding that love is not an easy-going substitute for law, but it is the fulfilling of the law. The law is needed as a warning to those who are tempted to sin and as a pattern for those who are striving for righteousness. When we accept Christ, He writes His law in our hearts, and we obey it, not because of fear of penalty, but because of love for our Lord.

Book of the Covenant
Exodus 21-24

In the Ten Commandments, God gives the law in outline. In Chapters 21 to 23 He gives the law in detail. At the conclusion of these chapters, we have promises given as to the presence and guidance of God and warnings against yielding to the temptation of forsaking God. After the people had promised obedience, Moses (in Exodus 24) **ratified** the covenant by sacrificial blood. The actions related to covenant-making recorded here provided a way for its significance to be explained and its seriousness to be remembered. Other references to covenant-making fill the Scriptures, especially in the account of the life of David.

ratified - confirmed; officially approved

Long Meeting

In the last part of Exodus 24, God called Moses up into the mountain to be alone with Him for forty days. At this time, God gave Moses the pattern for the tabernacle to be built by the children of Israel at Sinai. Moses left Israel under the authority of Aaron and Hur while he was on the **summit**, but their leadership did not keep the people from sinning. More about that later.

summit - highest point

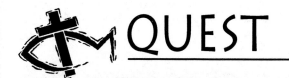# QUEST

Questions

Study Procedure: Read the Scripture references before answering questions. Unless otherwise instructed, use the Bible only in answering questions. Some questions may be more difficult than others but try to answer as many as you can. Pray for God's wisdom and understanding as you study and don't be discouraged if some answers are not obvious at first. Do not read the study notes for this lesson until AFTER you have completed your questions.

Day One: Vocabulary Review: Fill in the blanks with these vocabulary words.

MEMORY: GALATIANS 3:24

summit   Shekinah   covenant   patriarch   tyranny   explicit   ratified

1. The Ten Commandments were not general suggestions but _____ commands.

2. The visible presence of God around Sinai was called _____.

3. When the people agreed to the terms of God's _____, it was

   _____ by the sprinkling of blood.

4. Moses went to the _____ of Mt. Sinai to talk with God who had also talked

   long before to the _____ Abraham.

5. Without Christ's help, sin and death rule over us with _____.

6. After considering from your notes the importance of the Ten Commandments, do you think they

   should still be memorized in our church schools and the meaning taught to our young people?

   Give a reason for your answer. _____

   _____

   _____

   _____

Day Two:

MEMORY: 2 CORINTHIANS 6:16

1. Read Chapters 25-31 of Exodus. Do not, at

   this reading, try to remember all the construction details. As you read, write down the general

   topics covered. If you have a Bible with "headings," you may list these.

   a) Chapter 25 _____

   _____

   b) Chapter 26 _____

   c) Chapter 27 _____

   _____

   d) Chapter 28 _____

   _____

59

e) Chapter 29 _____

f) Chapter 30 _____

_____

g) Chapter 31 _____

Day Three:

MEMORY: PSALM 108:3-4

1. From Exodus 25:2, from whom was Moses to receive an offering? _____

_____

2. Where do you think the children of Israel got the materials for the construction of the tabernacle? _____

3. Make a list of the following, noting references. (Most come from Exodus 25.)

a) metals used in building the tabernacle _____

b) textile fabrics _____

c) skins used _____

d) wood _____

e) three things used for the anointing of the priest and burning in the tabernacle

_____

f) the gems _____

g) skills needed to build the tabernacle and its furnishings (Read Exodus 31.) _____

_____

Day Four: Match the following:

MEMORY: JOHN 1:14

_____1. the ark of the testimony

_____2. the table for the showbread

_____3. the gold lampstand

_____4. the altar of burnt offering

_____5. the tabernacle

_____6. the court of the tabernacle

_____7. the mercy seat

_____8. the laver

a) acacia wood table, covered in gold, with a molded frame around it

b) series of ten large fabric panels, attached together by clasps, made of expensive fabric and exquisitely embroidered designs, laid over gold-covered wood panels in silver sockets

c) gold chest, approximately 3 3/4 feet long by 2 1/4 feet wide and high

d) a solid gold lid with a gold cherub at each end

e) a seven-lamp gold stand, made of about 75 pounds of gold

f) altar of acacia wood, covered in bronze with a horn at each corner

g) huge wash basin made of brass, kept in outer court

h) a rectangle of linen, like a fence, 150 feet by 75 feet

Day Five: Read Hebrews, Chapters 8-10

1. According to the above Scriptures, what purpose did the tabernacle in the wilderness have in fulfillment of the new covenant?

MEMORY: HEBREWS 10:19-22

_____

_____

_____

2. Workmen were appointed and equipped to construct the tabernacle. Give their names and the tribes from which they came (Exodus 31). _____

_____

3. In the latter part of Exodus 31, what commandment did God emphasize? Why? _____

_____

_____

_____

4. After God gave Moses the pattern for the tabernacle, what else did He give him? _____

_____

5. Use Exodus 25:2 and Exodus 25:40 to summarize some important truths from this lesson.

_____

_____

_____

_____

_____

_____

6. Now take a few minutes to read your study notes for this lesson.

Notes

The Covenant Expressed: The Law and the Tabernacle

Israel as Unique

Israel was never meant to be ordinary. From her beginning she was created to be a holy nation, the chosen race, the possessor and messenger of salvation for all the nations of the earth. Moses, the deliverer of the people, by the power of God, led Israel to Sinai where the people were set apart as a holy nation. It was at Sinai that Israel heard and accepted the privileges and responsibilities of the covenant.

The covenant or holy contract that God clearly communicated to Israel through His laws, enabled Israel, as no other nation before her, to see His wisdom, holiness, purpose, power, and love toward her.

The covenant or holy contract that God clearly communicated to Israel through His laws, enabled Israel, as no other nation before her, to see His wisdom, holiness, purpose, power, and love toward her. She could know her God and rest securely on His ability to keep all the promises of the covenant. Israel pledged to submit to His commandments, restrictions, and sacrifices.

The Law Recorded

A large portion of the Pentateuch, the first five Biblical books, was given to the writing of the law, Moses being the communicator or mediator of it. The code of laws in the Pentateuch was interwoven into the framework of the history of the children of Israel. Laws intermixed with history; laws were repeated and inserted as they were given by God to Moses for the people during the years of desert wanderings.

moral - relating to principles of right and wrong

Three Divisions of the Law: Moral, Ceremonial, and Civil

1. The Ten Commandments form the **moral** law given to govern the behavior of Israel toward God as their Supreme Ruler and to each other as His children. The Ten Commandments required a love of God, love of neighbor, reverence for old age, forgiveness of injuries, rendering of good for evil, kindness, compassion and hospitality. Through this moral law, God revealed that He requires more than an **external** religious worship; He also demands a right attitude toward others. The moral law represented the love of God as a practical principle; it was absolute and eternal.

external - outer; that which can be seen

rites - formal or ceremonial actions or procedures

2. The ceremonial law involved a variety of **rites** and ceremonies which pointed distinctly to Christ, the expected Messiah. Specifically, it had to do with the priest, the tabernacle, the sacrifice, and other religious rites and services. Since the tribe of Levi was employed in these services, this law is sometimes referred to as the Levitical Law. The priesthood itself was confined to Aaron and his descendants. The object of this law was to keep the Jews from idolatry and remind them of the necessity of **atonement** for sin. It also taught them that God's holiness required adjustments on their part, if they were to approach Him safely and reverently. The requirements of this law were fulfilled for us through Jesus Christ, our High Priest.

atonement - reconciliation; restitution for an offense

civil - relating to citizens

theocratic - governed by God or His chosen representative

3. The **civil** law was like a constitution which set Israel apart as a distinct **theocratic** nation, with God as Supreme Ruler. Civil law related to the political and **judicial** aspects of the Hebrew people's lives: the ownership of the soil, its sale, redemption, and inheritance; **domestic** circumstances; servants or slaves, their treatment; debts, lending of money and its recovery; and the rights of the poor, the stranger, the sick, and the old. These laws were closely connected with

judicial - the function of judging

domestic - of or relating to the household or family

the moral laws, and they demanded obedience and faithfulness to God and kindness to their fellowman. It is interesting to note that our laws today can be traced to the basic principles of these laws.

Relevance of the Law Today God required obedience to the law for two reasons given in Exodus 20:2: (1) Because of who He is: *"I am the Lord your God"* (2) Because of what He has done: He *"brought you out of the land of Egypt, out of the house of bondage."* Christians could point to these, too, since He is our Lord and made us free from the slavery of sin. We no longer follow the rituals of the Old Testament law, but we can still learn from the moral truths they illustrated. We must know Jesus Christ and abide in Him, for obedience to all God has for us through His Word is not just a matter of religious activity. First, it involves a transaction in the heart by receiving Jesus Christ as Savior. Next, obedience to the true purpose of the law should show in loving actions toward God and our fellowmen. Power to do this comes through the Holy Spirit, whom Christ promised to give to those who receive Him (Christ). The Spirit gives power to live for Christ and power to be a witness for Christ. Apart from an experience of salvation in Christ, it is impossible to live as God intended us to live.

Law and Prophecy The law made God's people realize that they needed help in coming to God. Like the hired Roman slave who walked the children to school (Galatians 3:24), the law was never given to save people but to take them to the One who could. The law was good and described God's will for us, but no human, except for the God-Man Jesus, could ever obey it perfectly, because to break any part was to break the whole (James 2:10). The death penalty was the required punishment for the law-breaker, but if every person received that penalty, no one would be alive to enjoy fellowship with God. Man needed a substitute: someone not only to bear the penalty of the broken law, but also to take his place, receive the death penalty he deserved, and still have enough "life" left over to rise again and keep the man from falling back into sin. That kind of Savior sounded too good to be true, yet every part of the tabernacle and every ceremony required of the priests was a symbol or prophecy identifying that Perfect One and describing His works. The law made clear man's need for a Savior, and prophecy—in words and symbols—described that Savior's identity and power. Have you realized your need for a Savior? You will never be good enough to keep the entire law, so its death penalty hangs over you. However, like the single entrance into the tabernacle which required passing the brazen altar, we can still enter God's presence through the door God opened by the death of Jesus. There is no other option (Acts 4:12).

The law made clear man's need for a Savior, and prophecy—in words and symbols—described that Savior's identity and power.

Note: A fuller study of the Ten Commandments will come later when they are repeated in Deuteronomy.

The Covenant Confirmed
Exodus 24:1-11

When the children of Israel had promised obedience, they were accepting the terms of God's covenant. This would correspond to the "I do" in our covenant of marriage. To impress these transactions on their hearts, Moses confirmed the covenant by solemn ceremonies.

1) He wrote all the conditions of the agreement and also the people's act of consent in a book.

2) Moses, as the mediator of the people, accepted the resolution of the people. Jehovah would be to the people the God of Israel, their King and Protector, and would fulfill to them all the promises made to their fathers.

3) The ratifying of the covenant could not be done without the shedding and the sprinkling of blood. The Hebrew word from which covenant comes is *berith* and means "to cut," implying that blood was a regular part of sealing a covenant in Bible culture. Moses built an altar and erected twelve pillars. The altar represented the throne of God; the twelve stones, the twelve tribes of Israel. These were the two parties who were to contract or enter into covenant. The animal was sacrificed, and then Moses sprinkled half of the blood on the altar and half on the people. This showed that God and the people were mutually bound by the covenant. God was bound to protect, support, and save them, and the people were bound to fear, love, and serve God in all He had said to them. This transaction was the most important in all of the history of Israel. What significance!

God was bound to protect, support and save them, and the people were bound to God to fear, love and serve God in all He had said to them.

Plan of the Tabernacle
Exodus 24:12-30:35
Materials Requested

During the forty days Moses remained on Mount Sinai, God gave him a pattern for the tabernacle, or mobile sanctuary. God did not want Israel to remain at Sinai. They were to continue on to the land of Canaan and God was to journey with them. He was to dwell in the midst of His people. The pattern for the tabernacle was the first ordinance given to Moses since the giving of the law. Moses, upon returning from the mountain, called upon the Israelites to contribute to the construction with a willing heart: offerings of bronze, silver, gold, jewels, fine linen, embroidered materials of all colors, spices, valuable skins, oils and incense. The overwhelming response of the people showed that their giving was from love of God and His service and with a desire for His presence to be with them. The amount of what the people gave was not stressed, but the right motive for giving was.

Workmen Inspired
Exodus 31:1-18

God gave Moses the plan for the tabernacle, but it needed willing men to follow the pattern. Not only the two superintendents, but also the entire crew of workmen, needed to be qualified and chosen for each division of work. God told Moses that He had called men to do this work and had prepared them in wisdom and understanding and in knowledge and in all manner of workmanship. This should mean something to us. God calls and prepares us for the work He wants us to do. This eliminates misfits in jobs. It eliminates people in jobs who are only there for the money or prestige. Christians doing jobs honestly and efficiently, called by God to work where they are, that is God's plan. There would be fewer nervous breakdowns and psychological problems in the world of work if we asked God to show us what *"good works"* He has *"prepared beforehand that we should walk in them"* (Ephesians 2:10). God has a plan and purpose for His people. How important it is to have His guidance in every aspect of living!

God calls and prepares us for the work He wants us to do.

Note: Since descriptions of the tabernacle, its furnishings, and the garments and functions of the priesthood are repeated, more notes on them will follow in later lessons.

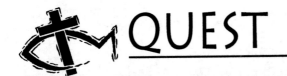

QUEST

Questions

Study Procedure: Read the Scripture references before answering questions. Unless otherwise instructed, use the Bible only in answering questions. Some questions may be more difficult than others but try to answer as many as you can. Pray for God's wisdom and understanding as you study and don't be discouraged if some answers are not obvious at first. Do not read the study notes for this lesson until AFTER you have completed your questions.

MEMORY: ISAIAH 1:18

Day One:

1. Vocabulary: Unscramble these words to complete their definitions.

   a) loarm _____ relating to principles of right and wrong

   b) teexlarn _____ outer; that which can be seen

   c) trise_____ formal or ceremonial actions or procedures

   d) ttnneeoam_____ reconciliation; restitution for an offense

   e) vilic_____ relating to citizens

   f) ccrtthieao _____ governed by God or His chosen representative

   g) ludicjai _____ the function of judging

   h) moditsce _____ of or relating to the household or family

2. Give the three-fold division of the Law and a brief description of each: (notes)

   a) _____

   _____

   b) _____

   _____

   c) _____

   _____

3. a) From Exodus 24, name the two parties involved in this contract or covenant, and describe how this covenant was confirmed. _____

   _____

   _____

   _____

   b) What significance does this have in light of New Testament teaching and the new covenant?

   _____

   _____

   _____

   _____

Day Two: Reread Exodus 24 and Exodus 32

MEMORY: HEBREWS 3:1-6

1. a) Find in Exodus 24 the last words the children of Israel said to Moses before he went up to spend forty days with the Lord on the mountain and write them below. _____

_____

b) Now find and write what they demanded of Aaron when Moses didn't return from the mountain when they thought he should. _____

_____

_____

_____

c) State in your own words their problem. _____

_____

_____

2. a) List some inconsistencies with what Aaron did and what he told Moses. _____

_____

_____

_____

_____

b) What was Aaron's problem as a leader? _____

3. What commandments did Aaron break? _____

_____

_____

_____

_____

4. What was the concern of Moses when God told him about the terrible sin of his people?

_____

_____

_____

_____

_____

5. What can we learn from the prayers of Moses about our approach to God? _____

_____

_____

_____

_____

Day Three:

1. Who accompanied Moses at least part way up the mountain and was waiting at his return?

   _____

2. What is interesting about Exodus 32:7 and 32:11? _____

   _____

   _____

3. What were the results of Moses' prayers before God for the children of Israel?

   _____

   _____

4. What expressions of indignation did Moses give as he came near the camp and saw what God

   had seen? _____

   _____

   _____

   _____

   _____

Day Four:

MEMORY: ISAIAH 26:3

1. What thoughts do you have about the call of Moses

   in the gate of the camp for *"whoever is on the Lord's side"?* _____

   _____

   _____

   _____

2. What happened to those who refused to be on the Lord's side? _____

   _____

3. Where was God placing responsibility for sin in His reply to Moses in Exodus 32:33?

   _____

   _____

4. Read Numbers 3:5-10. What reward did God give to the Levites for their faithfulness to Him when

   the nation worshiped the calf? _____

   _____

Day Five: Read Exodus 33 and 34

1. Give the verses from Exodus 33:1-10 that indicate Israel humbled themselves before God.

   _____

2. According to Exodus 33:11-23, what did Moses desire above everything else?

   _____

   _____

3. Comment on the significance of Moses having to be hidden by God in the "cleft of the rock" in order to see God's glory in Exodus 33:20-23. (See also 1 Timothy 6:14-16 and John 1:18.)

   _____

   _____

4. According to Exodus 34 did God renew His covenant to Israel? _____

5. What warnings did God give to the people about the land of Canaan? Give verses.

   _____

   _____

   _____

6. What was different about the countenance of Moses in Exodus 34 as he descended the mountain to the people, compared to his descent in Chapter 32? _____

   _____

   _____

7. Now take a few minutes to read your study notes for this lesson.

Notes

Broken Covenant

Israel's Impatience Yields Idolatry

Someone defined **character** as what we are when no one is watching. While Moses was in a forty-day conference with God on Mt. Sinai, receiving the detailed plans for the tabernacle of worship and the law, the children of Israel felt lost and insecure without a regular word from Moses. Unwatched by him, they revealed their immature spiritual character. His delay in coming down caused them to doubt his safety and their future without his leadership. They should have fought their doubts by recounting the truth about all that God had already done for them. Delay could have been spent in productive service, prayer, or praise, with no time given to fear and doubt.

character - distinctive quality

Short Memories

But that was not what happened. *"Come, make us gods...for as for this Moses, the man who brought us up out of the land of Egypt, we do not know what has become of*

They had freedom, food, and protection, all given to them miraculously by the living God, and in so short a time, with so little reason, they broke their vow of loyalty and asked for man-made gods.

futile - useless, ineffective

degradation - reduction to a lower rank or level

polytheism - worship of many gods

Moses pleaded the case of Israel with the argument God had given to him. He insisted that Israel was God's people and He had delivered them from Egypt with a mighty hand.

him" (Exodus 32:1). How soon they forgot! They had freedom, food, and protection, all given to them miraculously by the living God, and in so short a time, with so little reason, they broke their vow of loyalty and asked for man-made gods. This incident was not the first mention of idol worship in the history of Israel. Abraham's father Terah had owned idols as had Laban, the father of Rachel. (See Leviticus 17:7; Joshua 24:14; and Ezekiel 20:8 for other references to Israel's idolatry.) Paul warned in Romans that where man is unthankful to his Creator, idolatry follows: *"because, although they knew God, they did not glorify Him as God, nor were thankful, but became **futile** in their thoughts, and their foolish hearts were darkened...they changed the glory of the incorruptible God into an image made like corruptible man—and birds and four-footed animals and creeping things"* (Romans 1:21,23).

Weak Leadership

As a weak leader, Aaron played a leading part in this awful scene of **degradation** and wickedness. Instead of reminding the people of this being a violation of their solemn covenant with God and a breaking of the first three commandments, he gave in to their demands. Aaron may have felt that they would change their minds when he required them to give their personal jewelry, but they wholeheartedly responded because they wanted a visible idol. He misjudged the intensity of their desire and the weakness of their faith.

The symbol of the bull represented more than one Egyptian deity, and the sin of the Israelites was described as both idolatry and **polytheism**. This calf was to represent the gods who had brought them out of Egypt—the very gods against which the sovereign God had performed judgments. At this point Aaron announced a compromise, "a feast to the Lord." How much of our idolatry today do we sugar-coat with Christian associations or symbols? 1 John 5:21 says, *"Little children, keep yourselves from idols."*

Moses on the Mountain
Exodus 32:7-14

In the middle of the important matters about which God was informing Moses, God said, *"Go, get down! For your people. . .have corrupted themselves."* They had corrupted themselves by breaking their covenant promise to worship only the true and living God. In His anger, God called Israel Moses' people. But Moses prayed to God for Israel, changing the pronoun to "Your" people, and pleading for mercy for them. He did not "let God alone." We are reminded of Jacob when he said to the Lord as they wrestled, *"I will not let You go unless You bless me!"* (Genesis 32:26). Victory is gained when we mean business with God. Moses pleaded the case of Israel with the argument God had given to him. He insisted that Israel was God's people and He had delivered them from Egypt with a mighty hand. The three arguments Moses used can still be used today when we come before the Lord for forgiveness and restoration:

1. "They are Yours!" Israel was God's property. His past dealings with them had proven that (verse 11).
2. "The world will misunderstand Your actions." God's own glory was at stake because the nations who heard of His miraculous power in the miracles of Egypt would wonder if that power was now unable to keep Israel safe in the wilderness (verse 12).
3. "You promised." God's precious promises were pledged for their salvation (verse 13).

> **rebuke** - reprimand; reprove; correct

God heard Moses and did not **rebuke** him for his persistence or boldness. It is simply said that *"the Lord **relented** from the harm which He said He would do to His people."*

> **relented** - became less severe or harsh

Now how can the phrase *"the Lord relented"* be explained? Because He is infinite in wisdom, and we are finite, this is difficult. God does not relent as men do, as though He had made an error or had become unable to do as He planned. When God relented, He did not change His eternal purposes. In His mercy He allowed prayer or repentant actions to change the course of events. He never makes a mistake; yet He allows for prayer to matter. Alleluia!

Covenant Recap

To this point in our study of the Old Testament, we have had four covenants. (1) The covenant with Adam after the fall in Genesis 3:14-19. Blessings for faithfulness and curses for the covenant-breaker were traditional parts of any covenant. The covenant with Adam had both. Adam and Eve were clothed by God with animal skins, a reference to blood being shed by a substitute or representative to seal the covenant. (2) The covenant with Noah after the wickedness of man continued and promised a new start for mankind through the hereditary line of Noah and his three sons. There was a covenant sign given, the rainbow, to remind both covenant partners that a world-wide flood would not be used again. Following this, however, man continued in sin, breaking covenant, and receiving judgment. (3) God's covenant with Abraham contained a seven-part promise: (a) *"I will make of you a great nation;"* (b) *"I will bless you"* (c) *"and make your name great;"* (d) *"and you shall be a blessing."* (e) *"I will bless those who bless you,"* (f) *"and I will curse him who curses you;"* (g) *"and in you all the families of the earth shall be blessed."* This was an unconditional covenant. God took full responsibility for carrying it out, even to the point of putting Abraham to sleep

Blessings for faithfulness and curses for the covenant-breaker were traditional parts of any covenant.

while He sealed it. (See Genesis 15.) The disobedience of Abraham's descendants would never nullify God's promises given here. Disobedience would certainly bring consequences to the sinner and to the nation, but every promise given here would one day be completely fulfilled to a faithful remnant of Israel, no matter how small it might become. (4) The fourth covenant was the covenant given to them while Moses was their leader. God pledged Himself and His unlimited resources on their behalf, and they pledged to worship only Him and obey His laws for their nation. It took Israel only six weeks, while Moses was on the mountain where God was giving him instructions, to forget their covenant. Is it any wonder that God, in all His holiness, could not tolerate such a break in this contract by these people? So, the Lord offered to relieve Moses of his frustrating burden as their leader by **annihilating** them as a nation and beginning anew with Moses. It was here that Moses interceded for Israel.

> **annihilating** - reducing to nothing

Moses Comes Down
Exodus 32:15-35

Faithfully, Joshua waited for the return of Moses from the mount and was with him as he entered the camp of the Israelites. As they approached the camp, Joshua heard noise and thought it must mean war; Moses heard but recognized it as singing.

As the disgraceful scene came into full view, Moses threw down the tablets in righteous anger; they lay in pieces at the foot of the mountain. This action symbolized man's inability to keep the law given at Sinai. By the acts of the people and the conduct of Moses, the first use to which man put God's law was to break it. The children of Israel faced the most severe vengeance of an angry God.

> *The anger of Moses was the kind of anger we can have and not sin: angry at sin only.*

Calf Destroyed

Moses did not hesitate to confront the entire nation in her sin; his only weapon: holy anger. The anger of Moses was the kind of anger we can have and not sin: angry at sin only. Moses broke the tablets and burned the calf, thus showing appropriate anger at the awfulness of the sin committed. The scene before him was sickening; no one tried to stop him. He burned the idol, ground it to powder, put it in water, and made the people drink it. Then Moses turned to Aaron, who gave a very weak excuse for this awful sin and blamed the people. It was later revealed that the Lord almost destroyed Aaron at this time (Deuteronomy 9:20). What a natural thing it was to transfer the guilt of sin to others! Aaron was the leader and had power over the people, and yet he said the people overpowered him. Aaron's actions revealed the wicked results of compromising to please the people.

Help Enlisted
Exodus 32:26-29

"Whoever is on the Lord's side, come to me." The sons of Levi gathered about Moses. They had taken part in the rebellion but were willing to openly confess now that they were on the Lord's side. Those who openly and boldly stood in disobedience to the command to consecrate themselves to the Lord were slain. Judgment followed and three thousand fell by the sword.

It is still a very serious thing to take the commitment to Christ lightly. The call, *"Whoever is on the Lord's side,"* can still be heard. Christians are to be good soldiers of the cross of Jesus Christ. To be uncommitted is to be on the side that is not God's. One of our greatest problems today is that sin is not regarded in light of God's Word but by man's standard of right and wrong. To produce good soldiers, we must know that the battle against our enemy, Satan, is a fierce battle and that we war against that which destroys. This is the reason Paul warns us in Ephesians 6 to put on the whole armor of God, to be strong, and to stand. God knew, and Moses knew, that sin had to be dealt with, not smoothed over, covered up, or excused. Let us thank God that He still offers forgiveness to us when we confess our sins, and cleanses us from all such ungodly behavior (1 John 1:9).

The call, "Whoever is on the Lord's side," can still be heard. Christians are to be good soldiers of the cross of Jesus Christ. To be uncommitted is to be on the side that is not God's.

More Time on the Mountain
Exodus 32:30-35

The next day, Moses informed the people that he was going to approach God on their behalf and ask that God in mercy would receive them again into covenant. As Moses approached God this time, he did not refer to them as God's people, because he knew they were unworthy of that, but said *"these people."* He prayed that if there were no forgiveness, he should be put to death, too. We have the calm majestic reply to the request of Moses, *"Whoever has sinned against Me, I will blot him out of My book."* In other words, each man is responsible for himself. In His mercy God reduced the judgment, but there would still be punishment. This sin was remembered against Israel as evidenced in the Jewish saying, "No affliction has happened to Israel in which there was not some of the dust of the golden calf." God told Moses to *"go, lead the people to the place of which I have spoken to you."*

Israel Repents
Exodus 33:1 and 34:35

Although the children of Israel were covenant-breakers, God revealed Himself as the covenant-keeper. In fulfillment of the original promise, a special angel would go before Moses and the people to drive out the heathen from the promised land, but God could not be among the people without destroying them. When the people heard that God Himself would not be present among them on their journey, they mourned and repented. In their mourning, they stripped themselves of their ornaments in obedience to the demand of God.

Tent Meetings What is here called the tabernacle, or tent, was a place of meeting until the planned tabernacle would be constructed. It was removed and pitched outside the camp to show God's displeasure at Israel's recent sin. This tent probably had been known before as the tent of Moses. Here God met with His servant to communicate with him. God's presence in the pillar of cloud once more descended and stood at the tent door. This would represent to the people that although God had withdrawn from the midst of them, He was still accessible. The people stood and worshiped God against whom they had sinned. Every man worshiped in his tent door. It was in this tent of worship, out of the glory of His Presence, that God spoke to Moses as a friend.

Moses prayed for the renewal of the promise that God's presence would be in the midst of them. The Lord answered Moses, *"My Presence will go with you....I will also do this thing that you have spoken; for you have found grace in My sight, and I know you by name."* In response to Moses as mediator, God pardoned and restored full blessing. This pictures for us what happens today. Because the Lord Jesus has found grace before the Father, we are pardoned. *"There is no other name under heaven given among men by which we must be saved"* (Acts 4:12). This name is Jesus, the Mediator between God and man.

God's Glory Revealed
Exodus 33:18-23
"Please, SHOW ME YOUR GLORY." Had Moses not seen the glory of the Lord? Yes, more than perhaps any other man; yet God, knowing Moses' heart, answered, *"I will show you My goodness,...My kindness...and My grace."* From the birthplace of the law came a profound revelation of God's mercy and grace. However, Moses could not have lived through a full revelation of God's perfect nature. God "filtered" His glorious attributes by placing Moses in the cleft or opening of the rocky mountain crevice. We, too, could never bear the unfiltered glory of God; so, God, in the fullness of time, broke open the "Rock of Ages" and placed all who believe and receive Him within the shelter of His presence. Jesus took the blast of God's holy justice on the cross in our place. Safe in Christ, we will not have to face the fires of eternal judgment but will enjoy instead God's goodness, mercy, kindness, and grace. "Rock of Ages, cleft for me! Let me hide myself in Thee!"

God's Law Rewritten
Exodus 34:1-9

Moses followed God's instruction to cut out two tablets of stone and was ready the following day to go and meet with God on Mount Sinai. God would supernaturally rewrite His words on them. God also renewed the covenant with His people Israel and promised that they would return to the land of Canaan. However, God warned Israel about her future in Canaan. The children of Israel were not to involve themselves with **pagan** beliefs or religious practices. They must do away with them. The people of God must be pure.

pagan - heathen; idolatrous

God's Leader Affected
Exodus 34:29-35

Two forty-day sessions with God would certainly change a person spiritually and emotionally, but Moses also changed physically. As he came down from the mountain, the people could tell by the glory shining from his face that he had been with God. He wore a veil when speaking to them, so as not to trouble them with his strange appearance. Paul, in 2 Corinthians 3:15-18, pointed out that the veil of Moses symbolized Israel's inability to comprehend all that God had for them, but that through Jesus, that veil can be taken off.

Two forty-day sessions with God would certainly change a person spiritually and emotionally, but Moses also changed physically.

Starting Over

Having repented and been restored to fellowship, Israel closed the door on this outbreak of idolatry, which was a sad interruption in its history. Yet, in spite of this sin, God displayed divine mercy in response to the prayers of Moses. With the break healed and the covenant restored, they could proceed with the construction of the tabernacle.

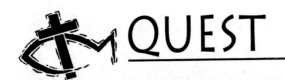

QUEST

Questions

Study Procedure: Read the Scripture references before answering questions. Unless otherwise instructed, use the Bible only in answering questions. Some questions may be more difficult than others but try to answer as many as you can. Pray for God's wisdom and understanding as you study and don't be discouraged if some answers are not obvious at first. Do not read the study notes for this lesson until AFTER you have completed your questions.

MEMORY: GALATIANS 3:24

Day One: Vocabulary Review

_____1. distinctive quality

_____2. reduction to a lower rank or level

_____3. worship of many gods

_____4. reprimand; reprove; correct

_____5. became less severe or harsh

_____6. useless, ineffective

_____7. reducing to nothing

_____8. heathen; idolatrous

a) futile

b) relented

c) rebuke

d) polytheism

e) degradation

f) pagan

g) character

h) annihilating

9. Review and record the different times that Moses interceded on behalf of Israel before God. Read the reference, then note the request, and answer to each prayer.

Reference	Moses' Request	God's Answer
a) Exodus 32:11-14		
b) Exodus 32:30-35		
c) Exodus 33:12-17		
d) Exodus 33:18-23		

Day Two: Read Exodus, Chapters 35–40 (in one sitting if possible)

1. Why do you think the law of the Sabbath was repeated at the very beginning of the construction of the tabernacle? _____

_____

_____

_____

2. From Exodus 35, list the verses and phrases that have to do with the attitude with which the people were to respond to the work of God. _____

_____

_____

_____

_____

3. In considering Exodus 35:31, using a dictionary, what is the difference in the meaning of the following words? Read Colossians 1:9.

    a) wisdom _____

    b) understanding _____

    c) knowledge _____

    d) Who is the source of wisdom, understanding and knowledge? _____

_____

Day Three: Reread Exodus Chapters 36-37   *MEMORY: COLOSSIANS 1:9*

    1. What were the results of the people giving with willing hearts? Give verses. _____

_____

_____

    2. Write down on a separate piece of paper the excuses the Israelites could have offered for not giving and compare them to the excuses used for not supporting God's work today.

_____

_____

_____

    3. Read Exodus Chapters 38-39. In Exodus 25-31 God gave to Moses the plan for the tabernacle. In Exodus 36-39 we have the actual _____ of the tabernacle.

    4. In what verse in Chapter 36 do we have the beginning of the construction of the tabernacle? Give the verse in Chapter 39 where the **work** is completed. _____

_____

    5. To whom did the workmen bring every **piece** of work for inspection and why? _____

_____

_____

Day Four: Read Exodus 39 and 40

1. From Exodus 39, list the reference each time you find *"as the Lord had commanded."*

    _____

    _____

2. How did Moses express approval to the people at the completion of the tabernacle? Read

    Exodus 39:43. _____

3. When God looked on the completed work, how was His approval expressed? _____

    _____

Day Five: Reviewing Exodus

MEMORY: PHILIPPIANS 4:19

1. God provided for all the needs of the children

    of Israel. From memory, write down the reasons for the giving of each of the following:

    a) The leadership of Moses _____

    _____

    b) The Passover _____

    _____

    c) The pillar of cloud and fire _____

    d) The escape route through the wilderness _____

    _____

    _____

    e) The law _____

    f) The plan for the tabernacle _____

    _____

2. God did a wonderful thing for us when He expressed Himself through covenant love. From your

    study of Exodus, summarize what you have learned about covenant-making._____

    _____

    _____

    _____

    _____

    _____

    _____

3. Now take a few minutes to read your study notes for this lesson.

Notes

The Building of the Tabernacle

Special Instructions Given

Exodus 35:1-8:31

Moses called the people together in order to instruct them in the detailed construction of the tabernacle, which was to be God's dwelling place among men. He first reminded them of the importance of keeping the Sabbath. In their zeal for building the house of God, they might forget God's requirements for its observance. This was the third time these instructions were recorded in Exodus. Since the next lesson will focus on the tabernacle and its special furniture, this lesson will emphasize the other truths of these chapters.

Giving

Exodus 35:4-29

"God loves a cheerful giver." (2 Corinthians 9:7). That New Testament thought appeared earlier in God's instructions for acceptable giving for the construction of the tabernacle. The attitude of the giver, not the size of the gift, was emphasized. Offerings were to be taken only from people who were *"of a willing heart."* Their hearts were stirred up as Moses explained the work that needed to be done. Then they responded and gave according to their ability. The more expensive gifts were given by the rulers; others did what they could in using their hands. ALL did what they could with a willing heart. The result was such an abundance that the people had to be asked to stop giving.

All did what they could with a willing heart. The result was such an abundance that the people had to be asked to stop giving.

Workers

Exodus 35:30-38:23

Not only the two superintendents, Bezalel and Aholiab, but also the entire crew of workmen were specially qualified and chosen for the various branches of work connected with the tabernacle and its furnishings. When God called them, He equipped them. The same is true today. It is important to do willingly the things we can do and to develop new skills when given the opportunity. We must offer to God what we have and trust Him to provide what we lack.

Some of the women offered their personal mirrors, made of bronze and highly polished. They were plentiful in Egypt and were made and used by the women there. This must have represented a personal sacrifice on the part of the women, but they gave what they had for this work. The mirrors were used in the laver, a piece of furniture in the outer court of the tabernacle. The laver has a very special significance which we will discuss in our next lesson.

Materials
Exodus 38:24-31

It is hard for us to comprehend the cost of the building of the tabernacle. The amount was great and gave real evidence of the dedication of God's people. It is interesting and significant that the building rested upon sockets made from silver given in equal amounts, half a shekel, by every man in Israel. The foundation of the tabernacle was symbolically linked with every man's need to have his life redeemed from death.

The foundation of the tabernacle was symbolically linked with every man's need to have his life redeemed from death.

Symbolism Explained

Before proceeding further, it will be helpful to look at the meanings commonly associated with the materials and colors used in constructing the different parts of the tabernacle.

MATERIALS:

Gold: divinity

Silver: redemption

Bronze: judgment (sturdy metal capable of withstanding great heat)

Wood: humanity

COLORS:

Purple: royalty

Blue: holy Spirit, heaven

Red: sacrifice

White: purity

Black: sinful man

artisans - skilled craftsman

Sewing for the Priests
Exodus 39:1-31

In Exodus 28:1-43 the instructions were given for making these garments, and in this chapter the work is being done by careful and skilled **artisans,** according to that pattern. Their obedience was emphasized with the repeating of the phrase *"as the Lord had commanded Moses"* in so many verses of Chapter 39.

The workmen had labored with diligence, and the job was perfectly completed. One can well imagine the joy Moses felt when he looked upon the ark, the curtains, the boards, the altar, the laver and the garments.

Careful Inspection
Exodus 39:32-43

The work of making the tabernacle and its furniture was accomplished in about six months. It was all presented to Moses for approval. He was the one who had seen the pattern and the only one qualified to pass final judgment. The workmen had labored with diligence, and the job was perfectly completed. One can well imagine the joy Moses felt when he looked upon the ark, the curtains, the boards, the altar, the laver and the garments. Moses blessed the workmen for their beautiful work to the glory of God. We may wonder why all the details of the tabernacle were given twice in these chapters. Perhaps we are to notice how God delights in and keeps exact accounts of the obedience of His people. Discipline is a forgotten art today. God requires that we be disciplined in our work and service to Him. When Christians are sloppy, lazy, or half-hearted in their work and witness, all of society suffers. God wants us to be fervent in spirit, serving the Lord in all that we do.

All Finished
Exodus 40:1-33

The tabernacle was to be erected on the first day of the month, exactly one year after the children of Israel left Egypt (Exodus 40:17). The furniture was to be placed carefully, and then Moses was to anoint the tabernacle and its furniture with the anointing oil. The oil, a symbol of the Holy Spirit, marked all that related to the tabernacle as sacred, set apart for God's use. Finally, Moses, Aaron and Aaron's sons were to wash at the bronze laver and thus begin their ministry as God had commanded.

Dedicated
Exodus 40:34-38

When Moses finished the work as instructed, the cloud which had faithfully guided Israel throughout their travels moved to the tabernacle. The glory of the Lord so filled the holy place that even Moses found it impossible to enter. Throughout all the journeys of the children of Israel through the wilderness, the Presence of God was with them in this way.

What's Next?

The book of Genesis detailed the fall of man through disobedience; the book of Exodus revealed blessings on Israel through obedience to the Word of God. After a study on the significance of the furniture in the tabernacle, Leviticus will follow with its description of a redeemed people worshiping God.

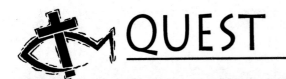

Questions

Study Procedure: Read the Scripture references before answering questions. Unless otherwise instructed, use the Bible only in answering questions. Some questions may be more difficult than others but try to answer as many as you can. Pray for God's wisdom and understanding as you study and don't be discouraged if some answers are not obvious at first. Do not read the study notes for this lesson until AFTER you have completed your questions.

Day One: Match the color or material with its meaning

_____ 1. divinity   a) bronze

_____ 2. redemption   b) wood

_____ 3. Holy Spirit, heaven   c) purple

_____ 4. purity   d) black

_____ 5. sinful man   e) gold

_____ 6. royalty   f) red

_____ 7. humanity   g) silver

_____ 8. sacrifice   h) white

_____ 9. judgment   i) blue

10. Summarize what you learned from Lesson 11 about the "attitude" of godly giving.

_____

_____

_____

_____

Day Two: Read Hebrews 9; Exodus 25:10-22;   MEMORY: JOHN 6:35

Exodus 37:1-2. **NOTE:** This lesson will focus on the seven pieces of furniture in the tabernacle and their significance as far as New Testament teaching is concerned: 1) the ark, 2) mercy seat, 3) the table of showbread, 4) the candlestick, 5) the altar of incense, 6) the laver, and 7) the altar of burnt offering.

1. According to Exodus 25, what was the special use of the ark? _____

_____

2. What was the lid or cover for the ark called? _____

3. According to the book of Hebrews, what other pieces were kept in the ark other than the

   testimony or law? _____

Day Three: Read Hebrews 9

MEMORY: HEBREWS 9:27-28

1. a) Where were the ark of the testimony and the mercy seat placed in the tabernacle?

    _____

   b) How often did the high priest go into the place where the ark and mercy seat were?

    _____

   c) What did he do there? _____

2. What verses in Hebrews 9 tell us the purpose of the Holy of Holies and of the first tabernacle?

    _____

    _____

3. Read Exodus 25:23-30. The second vessel of the tabernacle is the table of showbread. The ark and mercy seat speak to us of Christ and the throne of grace. What do you think would be the significance of this table? (John 6:31-37) _____

    _____

Day Four: Read Exodus 25:31-39;
Matthew 5:14; Revelation 1:12

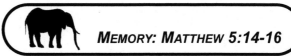

MEMORY: MATTHEW 5:14-16

1. a) What phrase(s) used in the description of the candlestick would indicate that it was a work of beauty? _____

    _____

   b) If the seven-branch candlestick is symbolic of the Holy Spirit, what do you think the flowers and fruit would represent in the life of a Christian? _____

    _____

    _____

2. Some believe that the candlestick could symbolize two things. What would they be? Give a reason for your answer. _____

    _____

    _____

    _____

    _____

    _____

3. Read Exodus 30:1-10. Where was the altar of incense placed in the Holy Place? _____

_____

4. According to the New Testament references Revelation 5:8 and 8:3-4, what was the significance

of the altar of incense? _____

_____

_____

_____

_____

5. What interesting thing happened at the altar of incense in Luke 1? _____

_____

_____

Day Five: Read Exodus 30:17-21; Exodus 38:1-8;

Psalm 24; Hebrews 4:12

MEMORY: HEBREWS 4:12

1. Where were the last two articles of furniture placed and what were they? _____

_____

_____

2. a) What is significant about the material used in the laver? _____

_____

   b) How is the laver symbolic of the Word of God? _____

_____

_____

3. Read Titus 3:5. What would the water in the laver be symbolic of? _____

_____

4. Read Exodus 27:1-8; Exodus 38:1-7. Was a sacrificial offering something new in worship to the

Hebrew people? Explain. _____

_____

5. Read Hebrews 10. The Old Testament teaching is specific about blood sacrifice for sin. According

to New Testament teaching, how were the demands of the law met so we no longer need to go

and offer the blood of animals for a sin offering? (Romans 8:1-4) _____

_____

6. Now take a few minutes to read your study notes for this lesson.

Notes

The Tabernacle and Its Furniture

General Description The tabernacle was constructed following God's plan for a portable tent, surrounded by a courtyard which was enclosed by a linen fence. The glory of God, cloud-like to human eyes, was visibly present over the tabernacle itself. Various terms are used to refer to it:

1) the "house or dwelling place of God" (Psalm 74:7),

2) the "tabernacle of meeting or assembly" (Exodus 40:34),

3) the "tent of the testimony" (Numbers 9:15; Exodus 38:21),

4) "the sanctuary" (Exodus 25:8).

This sanctuary, where the Holy One of Israel revealed Himself and entered into communion with His people, consisted of two parts:

1) The Most Holy Place, God's special dwelling place, entered only once a year on the Day of Atonement, by the High Priest, who was veiled in a cloud of incense and carried the blood of a sacrifice.

2) The Holy Place, where the priests, acting as mediators and intercessors for the people, drew near to God.

The glory of God, cloud-like to human eyes, was visibly present over the tabernacle itself.

Tabernacle Proper The tabernacle itself consisted of curtains of fine linen, which were woven with colored figures of cherubim. These were supported by a rectangular structure of boards, to define and support the Holy Place and the Most Holy Place. The tent was to be a true tent of goats' hair cloth. The covering was to be of red rams' skins and badgers' skins to be spread over the goats hair tent as an additional protection against the weather. The tabernacle apparently had no floor but the ground. What a contrast this must have been to the beautifully embroidered curtains and golden vessels!

Outer Court The outer court, outlined by the linen fence, was for the people. The Holy Place was for the priests, and the Most Holy Place was the dwelling place of God. Before the Holy of Holies, separating the two compartments of the tabernacle, hung a magnificent curtain, or veil. When Jesus said, while hanging on the cross, *"It is finished,"* this **veil** was torn from top to bottom, a supernatural act (Luke 23:45 and Matthew 27:51). This signified that from that time on, all distinction between the outer and inner court—the Holy of Holies and the Holy Place—was eliminated. Until Christ came, this veil remained in place, first in the tabernacle and later in the temple. Hebrews 10:19-22 states, *"having boldness to enter the Holiest by the blood of Jesus, by a new and living way which He consecrated for us, through the veil, that is, His flesh,...let us draw near."*

When Jesus said, while hanging on the cross, "It is finished," this veil was torn from top to bottom, a supernatural act.

Purposes Revealed

The object and design of the tabernacle was to provide a central place for God to reveal Himself to the Israelites, so that He could communicate with them. It was an act of grace; God did not have to reveal Himself visibly, but His love motivated Him to do so. There was intentionally only one tabernacle constructed to serve the whole nation. Since the days of Cain, people had shown a tendency to design their own forms of worship, but the tabernacle united them in the only acceptable worship of the true and living God.

The tabernacle, like the more permanent temple that followed, was a spectacular illustration of the plan of God to dwell with man. John's gospel recorded that *"the Word became flesh and dwelt (tabernacled) among us,...full of grace and truth"* (John 1:14). God took up His dwelling among men in the person of Jesus Christ so that men might draw near and have fellowship with God through His Son. The Old Testament tabernacle was a pattern for what was fulfilled in Christ. Each believer in Christ becomes a *"temple of the living God"* (2 Corinthians 6:16).

The priesthood, sacrifices, and altar pointed to the Person and work of the Lord Jesus Christ.

The priesthood, sacrifices, and altar pointed to the Person and work of the Lord Jesus Christ. The court, with the altar of burnt offering, was the place by which Israel approached God. In the Holy Place, they held communion with God and in the Most Holy Place the Lord Himself visibly revealed His presence in the Shekinah resting on the mercy seat, which covered the ark where the law was kept. Every part of the tabernacle reminded the people that God had made a way for them to know Him and to be accepted by Him.

Furniture of the Tabernacle Ark and Mercy Seat
Exodus 25:10-22; 37:1-9

The Most Holy Place or Holy of Holies was where the symbol of God's presence appeared. The compartment itself was a perfect cube of ten cubits or fifteen feet. Its only furniture was the ark of the covenant and its lid of gold called the mercy seat. When the High Priest entered on the Day of Atonement, he brought with him, along with the blood of a sacrificial animal, a bowl of incense from the altar of incense which stood outside the veil of the Holy of Holies.

The ark was the most excellent of all the holy things in the tabernacle, and the reason for which both the tabernacle and temple were built. The special place of God's presence within the tent was to be over the ark or chest containing the Ten Commandments, written on both sides by the finger of God on two stone tablets. However, because Israel had not been able to keep the commands of the law, the contents of the ark would remind God that they deserved death for breaking His covenant. But God, in His mercy, had provided a covering for the ark called the mercy seat. On this seat was sprinkled the blood of a perfect sacrificial animal once a year. God then looked at the blood covering the law and was satisfied that the penalty had been paid, and He withheld judgment from His people for another year. It is important to know that another word for mercy seat is **propitiation**, which means covering. The New Testament declares that *"we have an Advocate with the Father, Jesus Christ the righteous, and He Himself is the propitiation for our sins."* God looked at Him and accepted His sacrifice; the death penalty all sinners deserved was satisfied by Jesus on the cross for all time. Like a supernatural filter, Jesus protected us from the wrath of judgment and allowed only the loving kindness of God to shine through. The ark and the mercy seat were on the mind of the Psalmist when he wrote, *"Righteousness and justice are the foundation of Your throne; mercy and truth go before Your face"* (Psalm 89:14).

> **propitiation** - an atoning sacrifice

God looked at Him and accepted His sacrifice; the death penalty all sinners deserved was satisfied by Jesus on the cross for all time. Like a supernatural filter, Jesus protected us from the wrath of judgment and allowed only the loving kindness of God to shine through.

The Two Cherubim
Exodus 25:18-22

At the two ends of the mercy seat and rising out of it, were two cherubim made of beaten gold with outstretched wings arching over the mercy seat. These figures seemed to be symbolic of the glorious power in which God accomplishes His purposes—by agents unseen—yet sure, efficient and effective. (For a very interesting New Testament picture of the mercy seat read John 20:12.)

The Table of Showbread
Exodus 25:23-30

The table of showbread stood on the right side of the altar of incense and was furnished with dishes, spoons, covers, and bowls of pure gold. Twelve loaves of bread or cakes of fine flour were placed on the table in two rows of six each. The bowls holding the pure frankincense were placed on top of the bread. Flasks contained a supply of wine for pouring into the cups or smaller vessels used for the drink offerings. The bread was eaten by the officiating priests after it was removed from the table each Sabbath. Leviticus 24:8 recorded that this bread was laid upon the table as an offering from the children of Israel by a perpetual covenant. It represented a percentage of their possessions which they set aside as God's. The incense represented prayer and devotion.

The Candlestick of Pure Gold
Exodus 25:31-39

The golden candlestick was placed on the left of the altar of incense and was made of pure gold. It had an upright stem, from which branched out three pairs of arms, each pair forming a semi-circle. Their tops came to the same level as the top of the stem making a total of seven lamps. There were oil vessels and lamp tongs, or snuffers, for trimming the seven lamps and dishes to carry away any debris. The office of trimming and lighting the candles was performed by the priest when he went into the sanctuary every day to offer incense. The candlestick symbolized the spiritual light of life. In the vision of the heavenly temple in the book of Revelation 1:4, John identified the seven candlesticks with *"seven Spirits who are before His throne,"* or the Holy Spirit in all His fullness. When John turned to see the voice that spoke to him, he saw seven golden candlesticks and in Revelation 1:20, they are explained as representing the seven churches. So, the candlestick of the tabernacle could doubly symbolize the Holy Spirit and believers. The candlestick was covered with fruit and flowers of gold. These speak to us of the fragrance and fruitfulness that results in an individual life or the life of the church when it experiences the graces of the Holy Spirit. Its fruits are those of holy living. The oil of the Holy Spirit being fed into the lamps gives spiritual light and knowledge. The Holy Spirit is the great source of all spiritual light. Do we need to evaluate our source of divine knowledge and spiritual light? The only way the world has of knowing the light of the gospel of Christ is through the individuals and the churches whose lamps are lighted by the Holy Spirit. In our dark world this knowledge should be a challenge to us.

The Altar of Incense
Exodus 30:1-10

The altar of incense was in the Holy Place and in front of the veil which concealed the Most Holy Place. On this altar Aaron was to burn incense in the morning and in the evening when he dressed the lamps. This act is symbolic of prayer. The Psalmist cried, *"Let my prayer be set before You as incense, the lifting up of my hands as the evening sacrifice"* (Psalm 141:2). The coals used to burn the incense on the golden altar were taken from the brazen altar and taught the Israelites the source and means of acceptable prayers and praise. We can only effectively pray to God because the sacrifice of Jesus has opened the way.

We can only effectively pray to God because the sacrifice of Jesus has opened the way.

The Bronze Altar
Exodus 27:1-8; 38:17

There were two main vessels in the court of the tabernacle: the laver and the altar of burnt offering. Both were made of bronze rather than gold or silver. The altar of burnt offering was the first article of furniture and was sometimes called the bronze or brazen altar. It was to this altar that the people could come. It was the basis for all the work of the tabernacle. The priests could not enter into the Holy Place unless they had presented a sacrifice on the bronze altar. By this symbolic act, the children of Israel were taught, and we too are taught, that the first thing a sinner must do before he can pray with acceptance is to identify with the sacrifice of Christ. The atonement God provides is free to all, without exception and without distinction. The priest would not examine the sinner, but the sacrifice. No other part of worship was accepted until the blood had been offered on the altar. Our prayers, our tears, our repentance, our faith, our words, our actions, our sufferings, our vows, our giving, our sermons—all have worth or merit only as they stand in relationship to the sacrifice Jesus offered on the cross.

The Laver
Exodus 30:17-21

The laver was the second article of furniture in the court. Like the word *lavatory*, its root meaning is *to wash*. Before the priests entered the Holy Place, they had to wash their hands and their feet. They had already come by way of the bronze altar and been identified with its sacrifice, but in their daily work, their feet and hands became dirty. They had to exhibit *"holiness to the Lord"* in their every undertaking. The laver represented the Word of God. We are saved and forgiven because of the blood of Jesus, but we are cleansed continually as we look into the Word of God, see our filthiness, confess it, and allow the Holy Spirit, represented by the water, to *"cleanse us from all unrighteousness."* The Scriptures do not save us, but without them, like the mirrored panels of the laver, we would not be aware that we needed to be saved and would not know how to turn to God.

Summary

In review, then, the tabernacle and the seven pieces of furniture illustrated the Christian experience. Entering by the one door, one stopped first at the bronze altar. Bronze could withstand high heat and so symbolized judgment on sin. The sacrificial animal was examined by the officiating priest and slain and offered there. The laver provided the necessary cleansing from the contamination of living and serving in a world where atonement was required for sin. The Holy Place, housing the golden candlestick, altar of incense, and table of showbread, pictured our ongoing relationship with God. His Spirit gave the light for service, allowing lives to produce fruit. Prayer rose before God like incense from the altar and was considered precious to Him. Lastly, the table holding the loaves of showbread spoke of the sustaining nourishment that fellowship and obedience to Him provide. The veiled Holy of Holies contained the most precious truth of God; all within was gold, the metal of royalty, holiness, and divinity. The judgment of God had been satisfied by the blood sprinkled on the mercy seat, covering the evidence of the broken law. Mercy was freed to shine powerfully from that seat of mercy. Now, for us, the veil is removed and we can boldly enter the throne room that this foreshadowed, to receive grace and help in time of need.

The judgment of God had been satisfied by the blood sprinkled on the mercy seat, covering the evidence of the broken law.

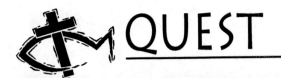QUEST

Questions

Study Procedure: Read the Scripture references before answering questions. Unless otherwise instructed, use the Bible only in answering questions. Some questions may be more difficult than others but try to answer as many as you can. Pray for God's wisdom and understanding as you study and don't be discouraged if some answers are not obvious at first. Do not read the study notes for this lesson until AFTER you have completed your questions.

MEMORY: ISAIAH 55:6-9

Day One

1. a) Make a sketch below of the tabernacle, including placement of the furniture.

   b) Define propitiation. _____

2. Explain below what purpose each of the seven pieces of furniture in the tabernacle served and what it symbolizes for Christians.

   a) bronze altar _____

   _____

   b) bronze laver _____

   _____

   c) golden candlestick _____

   _____

   d) golden altar of incense _____

   _____

   e) golden table of showbread _____

   _____

   f) golden ark of the covenant _____

   _____

   g) golden mercy seat _____

   _____

Day Two: Read Leviticus, Chapters 1-5

1. From these first chapters in Leviticus, list the offerings described and indicate which were voluntary and which were required.

MEMORY: ISAIAH 55:11

   a) Chapter 1 _____

   b) Chapter 2 _____

   c) Chapter 3 _____

   d) Chapter 4 _____

   e) Chapter 5 _____

2. You made a list of the offerings with their references from Leviticus 1-5. What do all five offerings have in common? _____

   _____

3. Read Hebrews Chapter 10. Which of the aspects or positions you just named did Christ become for us? Give reference(s) from Hebrews to substantiate your answer. _____

   _____

Day Three:

MEMORY: ISAIAH 64:8

1. In Leviticus 1, why do you think there were three categories or grades of giving as to the "burnt offering?" (an offering from the herd, an offering from the flock, an offering of a turtle dove or pigeon)

   _____

   _____

   _____

   _____

2. From a Bible dictionary, find the difference between clean and unclean animals. This will be helpful as we read about this distinction concerning sacrifice and food throughout the Word of God. _____

   _____

   _____

3. From Leviticus 4, list four classes of persons included in the "sin" offering. _____

   _____

   _____

4. Review Leviticus 5. In which of the offerings was there to be restitution? _____

   _____

Day Four: Read Leviticus, Chapters 6-9

1. In Leviticus 6, what offering is continually to be burning so that the fire never goes out?

    _____

2. From Leviticus 7:22-27, what two parts of the sacrifice were not to be eaten?

    _____

3. Read Levitucus 8:23. Specific parts of the priest were anointed. What do you think each of these
    represent as they related to the duties of the priest? _____

    _____

4.   What phrase is repeated over and over in Leviticus 8 and 9, which **emphasizes** the authority of
    the Word of the Lord? _____

5. What did Moses tell Aaron would happen after he finished offering **the required** sacrifices?

    _____

6. From Leviticus 9, give in your own words, the beautiful ending **to the service** of worship and the
    response of the people. Give verses where these are described. _____

    _____

    _____

Day Five: Read Leviticus 10

MEMORY: JEREMIAH 10:24

1. After reading Leviticus 10, explain in a word or
    two how worship and joy could change so suddenly to sorrow and death. _____

    _____

2. Immediately after the judgment on Nadab and Abihu, God gave a rule of conduct for priests,
    explaining its purpose. What was it, and do you think this had something to do with the
    previous incident? _____

    _____

    _____

3. Do you feel God has relaxed His requirement for holiness under the new covenant as far as false
    teaching and practices are concerned? _____

4. In the last verses of Leviticus 10, God's mercy was shown to the two younger sons of Aaron who
    did not precisely obey the laws of sacrifice. Why do you think they received mercy when their
    older brothers had received swift and deadly judgment for their actions? _____

    _____

    _____

5. What expression in Leviticus 10:19 showed Aaron's feeling of grief? _____

    _____

6. Now take a few minutes to read your study notes for this lesson.

Notes

A Nation in Training: Leviticus, Numbers, Deuteronomy

Introduction to Leviticus

Only the direct descendants of Aaron could be priests in the new tabernacle, but they needed more help than just their family could give for the many duties relating to the **worship rituals** and transportation of the tabernacle that the law required. The tribe of Levi, to which Moses and Aaron belonged, chose the "Lord's side" in the episode of the golden calf and was rewarded with the life-long honor of assisting in the Lord's work. This book of Leviticus received its name in later years because much of it relates to the responsibilities of the tribe of Levi or the Levites who helped in worship. Leviticus could be thought of as a training manual for priests and **Levites,** who were responsible for teaching all the people about the proper way to approach God.

> **worship** - respect or reverence paid to a divine being

> **rituals** - the established forms for a ceremony; formal, repeated series of acts

> **Levites** - members of the tribe of Levi; assistants to the priests

To worship is to declare with words and actions the "worth-ship" or worthiness of the person or thing involved. God told Israel, through the laws He gave to Moses, what was acceptable and was unacceptable in the area of worship. Moses was to see that the nation's worship leaders were properly informed of these laws. Jewish historians recorded that it was Leviticus that was first taught to children when they started their religious education. How appropriate, since all true learning must begin with a correct view of the holiness of God and an understanding of His plan for overcoming the natural unholiness of man.

To worship is to declare with words and actions the "worth-ship" or worthiness of the person or thing involved.

How to Get Close and Stay Close to God

From the past weeks of study we have seen that Israel, like people today, had a tough time staying right with God. They seemed to forget so quickly who He really was and overlook too often how unworthy they were to be chosen, blessed, and protected by Him. Ingratitude for His goodness seemed to follow their daily preoccupation with personal needs. God knew that man could not be "good" without His constant help. He also knew that man would forget to come to God for that help without a regular reminder. The book of Leviticus helped set up required rituals on a daily, weekly, monthly, and yearly basis to continually keep before the people their need for God's mercy, forgiveness, and very presence among them. The tabernacle itself would be set up as the center of their every encampment. They would see, hear, and smell daily the necessary work of sacrifice. They would be taught regularly the truth about the immeasurable worth of the God who chose them. They would have little excuse for not being aware of who God was and how He could be approached appropriately and effectively for regular worship and thanksgiving or for periodic help in time of need. Like a loving father, God did not just want to help

His people out of trouble, He wanted to keep them out of trouble. He did not want just to forgive them for sin, but to keep them from sinning. He did not just want them to come to Him for an occasional visit, but to live with Him always.

Two and Two

Two main topics summarize the teachings of Leviticus: **Worship:** How to come near to God (Chapters 1-16) through sacrifice. **Walk:** How to stay close to God (Chapters 17-27) through obedience. The two key verses summarizing these are Leviticus 17:11: *"For the life of the flesh is in the blood, and I have given it to you upon the altar to make atonement for your souls; for it is the blood that makes atonement for the soul;"* and Leviticus 20:7,8: *"Consecrate yourselves therefore, and be holy, for I am the Lord your God. And you shall keep My statutes, and perform them: I am the Lord who sanctifies you."*

"For the life of the flesh is in the blood, and I have given it to you upon the altar to make atonement for your souls; for it is the blood that makes atonement for the soul."

Does Leviticus Help us Today?

While it is true that Christians do not have to obey the many ceremonial laws requiring sacrifices and periods of separation described in Leviticus, they are still guided by the principles behind these activities. Continuing His word-picture teaching technique, God used the ceremonial system as an effective visual aid for these important truths:

1. Sin separates man from God. Because He is holy, He cannot overlook sin but must have His justice satisfied.
2. Since blood is necessary for life, it becomes the representative or substitute for a life. Without the shedding of blood, there is no forgiveness of sin.
3. Sin is expensive; it always costs someone something.
4. Man cannot clean himself up enough ever to approach God on his own; he can only approach God by accepting God's plan of approach: offering a sacrificial substitute to pay the price for sin, then receiving an inward change of heart, provided only by God's Holy Spirit, to maintain the closeness that the sacrifice provided.

The Five Kinds of Offerings
Leviticus 1:1-7:38

A sacrifice acceptable to God was the basis for all true worship. The excellence of the sacrifice declared to witnesses the worth of the One being worshiped. The use of sacrifices was not new in this period of the history of Israel but could be traced back to the very beginning of the history of mankind (Genesis 4:4 and 8:20). Here in the book of Leviticus, God gave a detailed description of what He would accept in the way of worship through sacrifice.

The Burnt Offering: Voluntary and Perfect
Leviticus 1:1-17

This offering's name literally meant "ascent" since the entire offering, except the blood, was burned on the bronze altar and ascended before God in smoke. The whole burnt offering pictured for us how we are to give our all to God, holding nothing back. In Romans 12:1 Paul urged us to *"present your bodies a living sacrifice to God"* as the least we should do in light of His great worth.

There were two basic requirements for a burnt offering. **First**, it had to be voluntary: the action of a willing heart responding in true worship to God. Even though right actions were emphasized through these rituals, heart attitude was always most important to God. **Secondly**, it had to be perfect, *"a male without blemish"* (Leviticus 1:3). This could be a three-year-old bull, a one-year-old sheep or goat, or a turtle dove or young pigeon. Whether bull, ram, goat, or bird, one thing was required: it was to be physically perfect. This requirement made the sacrifice a more fitting type of the Lamb sacrificed to take away the sins of the world in the New Testament. Jesus was perfect and willingly laid down His life.

Even though right actions were emphasized through these rituals, heart attitude was always most important to God.

The Grain Offering
Leviticus 2

The second type offering was the grain or meal offering, which was a return to God of a portion of fine flour, baked goods, or ears of grain in gratitude for His provision. Oil, frankincense, and salt were to be added to this offering. Part of the grain and oil and all of the frankincense were to be burned on the altar as a gift to God. The remaining portions were given to the priests to eat.

Leaven and honey were not to be added to this offering. Leaven, because of its permeating influence, was often used in Scripture as an emblem of pride, hypocrisy, malice and wickedness (1 Corinthians 5:8). The **prohibition** of the leaven and honey was only for the usual meal offering and did not apply to the offering of the firstfruits of everything which had to be presented before the Lord (Exodus 23:16; 34:22; Leviticus 23:17).

prohibition - an order to restrain or stop

Eating salt together in the East was a form of covenant-making. "A covenant of salt" stood for purity and permanence. Salt was used in the sacrifices and offerings of the Israelites, probably with the idea of depicting honor and loyalty. It was the one symbol that was never absent from the altar of burnt offering, showing the everlasting love of Jehovah for His people.

The peace offering was brought to show gratitude on the part of the individual for his peace with God.

The Peace Offering
Leviticus 3:1-17; 7:11-30

The peace offering was brought to show gratitude on the part of the individual for his peace with God. It was offered not to make peace with God but to celebrate joyfully the peace already made through the covenant. This offering pictured God already present in His house and inviting the worshiper to feast with Him. Peace offerings were slain with the same ceremonies as the burnt offering, but only choice parts were burned on the altar: the fat, the kidneys, and in the case of a lamb, the rump. These parts are the delicacies of the feast and were therefore offered to Jehovah. The breast and the shoulder were the portion for the priests, who were to eat them in a clean place with their families. They were called the wave-breast and the **heave**-shoulder from the motion used in offering them before the Lord. The priests also took one of the unleavened cakes which was offered as a meal offering with the peace offering after having **heaved** it before the Lord. At this feast there was friendship, joy, and thankfulness.

heave - to lift up

The Sin Offering

The sin offering spoke of the fact that a covenant between God and man had been broken by man. It could only be knit together through the shedding of blood. In the ceremony accompanying this sin offering, the blood of the sacrifice was sprinkled by the priest in front of the sanctuary, on the horns of the altar of incense, and at the foot of the altar of burnt offering. The shedding of blood, the symbol of life, signified what the offender deserved because he had sinned and that the death of the sacrificial animal was accepted in his place by God's mercy. The sin offering gave witness to the fact that sin existed in man, that the wages of sin was death, and that God had provided an acceptable payment by the **vicarious** suffering of an appointed victim.

vicarious - suffered in place of another; serving as a substitute

Its Placement

There was an interesting order given to the offerings in Scripture. The sin offering followed the other three mentioned, but as a matter of ritual, was ordinarily offered first. The other types of offerings had been in use before this time. The sin offering was a new thing and was instituted because of the law. Paul wrote in Romans 7:7 that he was not even aware of his sin until the law revealed what sin was. With the law came knowledge of how far off God's mark man had moved. The sin offering provided a way back, and everyone needed it: *"all have sinned and fall short of the glory of God"* (Romans 3:23). The sin offering was a *"shadow of things to come"* (Colossians 2:17).

With the law came knowledge of how far off God's mark man had moved. The sin offering provided a way back, and everyone needed it.

The offending person, priest, or ruler had to bring his own sin offering. He had to personally lay his own hands upon its head and have a genuine concern for his sin. So it is that all must come to the foot of the cross and there by faith accept personally the sacrifice of Christ as the atonement for sin. 1 John 1:9, *"If we confess our sins, He is faithful and just to forgive us our sins and to cleanse us from all unrighteousness."* Christ's atonement for sin can only benefit those who personally receive it.

The Trespass or Guilt Offering
Leviticus 5:14-19; 6:1-7; 7:1-7

To **trespass** meant to go across; in relation to sin it meant to go across the boundary God had set in His Word for what was right and acceptable. Trespasses in Scripture were debts—definite acts of wrong or evil. In the case of trespasses against God, sacrifice was required first, then restitution. In the case of trespasses against man, which were also counted as against the Lord, **restitution** was required first, then sacrifice. This offering was closely connected with the sin offering and helped teach that while a sinner needed God's mercy to "fix" what sin had broken in the spiritual world, he was required to "fix" what he had broken in the physical world through replacement or repayment. Sin always costs someone something.

trespass - to go across; to sin

restitution - to restore to a former state; refund

To trespass meant to go across; in relation to sin it meant to go across the boundary God had set in His Word for what was right and acceptable.

Five Offerings Picture Christ

In review, the whole burnt offering symbolized Christ's total submission to the Father's will. The meal or grain offering without yeast or honey represented Christ's sinless service. The peace offering depicted the on-going fellowship with God that Christ's death provided for us. The sin offering emphasized Jesus bearing all our sins and guilt, while the trespass offering spoke of Christ's ability to repair the damage sin caused in our lives. Christ did it all for us.

Consecration of Aaron and His Sons
Leviticus 8:1-9:24

The ceremony of consecration took place at the door of the tabernacle. The entire congregation of Israel came together to witness this event. Aaron was called by God for this office of high priest and was commended for doing *"all the things that the Lord had commanded by the hand of Moses."* Aaron's sons were associated with him in the work, holding their positions because of their relationship to their father. There is great significance in these chapters; our High Priest, Jesus Christ, is pictured in every priestly work in the tabernacle. (Read Hebrews 7.)

Death of Nadab and Abihu
Leviticus 10:1-20

This incident occurred before Aaron had even completed his first day of ministry following the consecration ritual. He had just offered the sacrifices, entered into the Holy Place with Moses, and returned to the court of the tabernacle. The people had been standing in silent expectation. God had shown His approval and His confirmation of Aaron in his

presumptuous -
overstepping due bounds;
taking liberties

priestly acts by sending down fire to burn up the sacrifices which had been laid in order on the altar. Then a **presumptuous** act on the part of his two oldest sons changed the day from one of rejoicing to one of mourning. Nadab and Abihu, two of Aaron's sons just anointed as priests, took it upon themselves to improvise on God's laws for offerings, xand brought "profane fire" into the worship services. Their innovation brought them a sudden, fiery death. So, at the very beginning of the tabernacle era, God condemned man-made worship. The priest and the people were taught in a way that would not soon be forgotten: man cannot decide what will be pleasing to God but must obey what God has said is pleasing to Him in His Word. We are reminded at this point of the apostle's words, *"let us have grace, by which we may serve God acceptably with reverence and godly fear. For our God is a consuming fire"* (Hebrews 12:28-29).

What Happened

There seems a possibility, from the verses that follow this incident, that Nadab and Abihu had over-celebrated with intoxicating drink during the feast of the peace offering; because, immediately afterward, Moses issued the law against the priests drinking wine and strong drink, since it would affect their discernment between holy and unholy. The worship of God still requires a clear mind and demands a pure and undivided heart. Proverbs 31:5 says, *"Lest they drink and forget the law, and pervert the justice."* Ministers are admonished to be *"sober-minded,...not given to wine"* (1 Timothy 3:2-3).

The Work Continued

God desires of us a will to serve Him with an uncomplaining faith, accepting His decisions even when they are painful and perplexing.

Moses recognized the holy justice of God and warned Aaron not to grieve as if he had been wronged but instead to remember his anointing as priest. Others would do the grieving for Nadab and Abihu. So, in spite of this great emotional trauma, Aaron called his other sons to continue in the service of the Lord. God desires of us a will to serve Him with an uncomplaining faith, accepting His decisions even when they are painful and perplexing.

What would be the verdict today if God would judge our sense of reverence and godly fear as we come to worship Him? Would He approve of what we do in the name of Christian worship or would He find it too man-made? This question is something we need to consider.

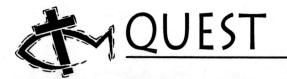 QUEST

Questions

Study Procedure: Read the Scripture references before answering questions. Unless otherwise instructed, use the Bible only in answering questions. Some questions may be more difficult than others but try to answer as many as you can. Pray for God's wisdom and understanding as you study and don't be discouraged if some answers are not obvious at first. Do not read the study notes for this lesson until AFTER you have completed your questions.

Day One: Vocabulary Review: Fill in the blanks

MEMORY: HEBREWS 12:28

1. worship - respect or reverence paid to a _____ _____

2. rituals - the established _____ for a ceremony; formal, repeated _____ of _____

3. Levites - members of the tribe of _____; assistants to the _____

4. prohibition - an order to _____ or _____

5. heave - to _____ up

6. vicarious - suffered in _____ of another; serving as a substitute

7. trespass - to go _____; to _____

8. restitution - to _____ to a former state; _____

9. presumptuous - _____ due _____; taking liberties

10. What are the two main divisions of the book of Leviticus? _____

    _____

    _____

    _____

11. What one incident in particular from the last lesson would cause us to know that God does mean what He says in His Word about taking seriously our responsibility in our work for and worship of Him? _____

    _____

    _____

Day Two: Read Leviticus, Chapter 11

MEMORY: ROMANS 3:20

1. What one truth was God trying to impress on the hearts of the Israelites concerning the way to fellowship with Him? Give one verse from Chapter 11 that would be the key to this. _____

    _____

2. What was to be characteristic of the clean animals? _____

_____

3. What was to be characteristic of the clean fowl and fish? _____

_____

_____

Day Three: Read Leviticus, Chapter 12;

MEMORY: COLOSSIANS 2:11-12

Psalm 51:5

1. Find the reference in Genesis 17 that explains the purpose of circumcision mentioned in

Leviticus 12:3._____

2. God wanted people to have children and said that children were a blessing. Why then do you

think He required a sin offering after a birth? _____

_____

_____

_____

_____

3. Read Luke 2:21-24. What can you learn about Mary and Joseph from this passage?

_____

_____

_____

_____

Day Four: Read Leviticus, Chapters 13-15

1. Who was the one to diagnose a leprous person? _____

_____

2. Give the main symptoms of leprosy. _____

_____

3. If a person was found leprous, where was he to go? _____

4. Give the verse in Leviticus 14 which would indicate that the leprosy referred to was not always

incurable. _____

5. Besides the person himself, what other two things had to be examined for contamination of

leprosy? _____

Day Five: Read Leviticus 16 and Hebrews 9-10:15

1. Leviticus 16 describes the proper observance of the Day of Atonement. What warning is

   MEMORY: HEBREWS 10:14

   issued right at the beginning about approaching God *"inside the veil, before the mercy seat"?*

   _____

   _____

2. From Chapter 16, explain the selection and purpose of the scapegoat. _____

   _____

   _____

   _____

   _____

   _____

3. To be fully understood, the Day of Atonement described in Leviticus 16 should be studied along with the description in Hebrews 9-10:15 of Christ as our High Priest and atoning sacrifice. Put the appropriate verses from these chapters beside the following observations.

Israel's High Priest   **Reference**

    a) wore pure and spotless garments_____

    b) made atonement with blood of goat _____

    c) offered atoning sacrifice once a year _____

    d) entered the Holy of Holies, behind the veil _____

    e) sacrificed for the whole nation _____

    f) offers sacrifices repeatedly _____

Jesus, as High Priest   **Reference**

    a) had a pure and spotless character_____

    b) made atonement with His own blood _____

    c) made atonement once and for all time_____

    d) entered heaven itself _____

    e) sacrificed for the whole human race _____

    f) after offering the one sufficient sacrifice, sat down at God's right hand _____

4. Now take a few minutes to read your study notes for this lesson.

Notes

Holiness Required

No Area Unimportant

These chapters emphasized the truth that God is concerned with the total person, not just spiritually and emotionally, but physically as well. To be holy as God is holy, a person must be separate from the things God has declared to be unhealthy or unholy. The children of Israel were to learn that even the common business of eating was to be governed by holy laws. By obeying God's rules, they would learn the principles of holiness. He wanted their whole lives to be distinctly different from the idolatrous behavior around them and to be examples of purity in a very impure world.

He wanted their whole lives to be distinctly different from the idolatrous behavior around them and to be examples of purity in a very impure world.

Food Choices
Leviticus 11:1-43
Animals

The animals that the Hebrew people were permitted to eat could be classified as **domestic** and would have had the cleanest feeding habits. The clean animals were distinguished by two characteristics: (a) having divided or cloven hooves and (b) being ruminants or chewers of cud. The selection of these animals was simple and practical and the people could easily recognize them.

domestic - living near or about the habitations of man

Clean and Unclean Fish

All fish that had scales and fins would be considered clean and all others unclean. This distinction was also simple and clear.

Clean and Unclean Fowl

The law having to do with birds was different from the others because it did not give any particular distinction of clean or unclean. It prohibited certain known species of birds, leaving the impression that all others were permitted. The unclean birds were those who lived on dead flesh or garbage.

Insects and Creeping Things

This class of creatures was not to be eaten with the exception of locusts, crickets, and grasshoppers.

Why These Rules?

The dietary laws for the children of Israel revealed first God's concern for the bodies of His people. We, too, should not carelessly disregard or neglect our bodies. Secondly, these laws helped Israel to live separately from the nations around them, since observing these rules would make it very difficult to mingle freely with other groups.

The laws God gave to His people effectively promoted sanitation and separation, as well as the larger concept of holiness. They were to avoid uncleanness not only for reasons of physical health but also for the reason that God is holy and they were in covenant with God: *"And everyone who has this hope in Him purifies himself, just as He is pure"* (1 John 3:3). We are no longer bound by the same ceremonial laws Israel followed, but since Christ has cleansed us with His blood, we must continue to be clean in thought, word, and deed.

Purification Laws at Childbirth
Leviticus 12:1-8

The Psalmist declared that *"children are a heritage from the Lord, the fruit of the womb is a reward"* (Psalm 127:3). There is no event more life-changing to parents than the birth of a child. The ritual of purification that was required for the mother at the birth of a child in no way implied that marriage and proper sexual relations were sinful. The birth of a child was considered to be a great blessing to the Hebrew people; not to have children was a disgrace. As the rite of **purification** was carried out, parents would be impressed with their moral and spiritual responsibility to the newborn child. Even though every child was born in sin, parents were taught to bring an offering that would "cover" that sin. Modern-day philosophy declares that children are born good and need only to be allowed to develop naturally, with few parentally-placed limits, to turn out just fine. Christian parents are more realistic than this. A child is born with a corrupt nature, completely self-centered, and must have parental guidance to counter-act this. Parents need to pray for their children, who have been born in sin that they soon will be "born again." Parents need to intentionally surround their children with godly instruction and example.

> **purification** - an act of removal of anything alien, improper, unnecessary, corrupting or otherwise damaging

Even though every child was born in sin, parents were taught to bring an offering that would "cover" that sin.

Does God Have Favorites?

The purification period differed according to whether the baby was a boy or a girl. The period the mother was kept apart from the regular routine was twice as long with a daughter. The reason was most likely God's thoughtful provision for protection of the mother in a culture that gave preference to sons. If a woman had a daughter, the husband might rush her too quickly into another pregnancy, in hopes of having a son. God protected the woman, legislating double-time apart for recovery, in case the husband was over-anxious and tempted to disregard the welfare of his wife.

Leprosy in People, Clothing, and Houses
Lev.13:1-59; 14:33-57

Two long chapters are devoted to the diagnosis and treatment of leprosy. Since leprosy was a contagious and often incurable disease, a person having it had to take many precautions so as not to spread it to anyone else. His appearance, even from a distance, had to advertise his affliction. He had to tear his clothes, shave his head, and cover his face. When he saw anyone approaching he had to warn them **audibly** by calling out, *"Unclean, unclean!"*

audibly - in a manner that can be heard

Some critics have argued that the disease described here in Leviticus is not the same as leprosy in the time of Christ. However, in Matthew 8:1-4 when a leper came to Jesus for healing, Jesus told him, *"Show yourself to the priest, and offer the gift that Moses commanded, as a testimony to them."* Jesus indicated that the disease He had healed was the same one covered by the law.

Learning from Leprosy

insidious -developing so gradually as to be well established before becoming apparent

As the ritual of purification and covenant circumcision enabled a child to start a new life, so the testing and cleansing rituals of the leper in Chapter 13 enabled him to rejoin the daily lives of God's people. Leprosy paralleled physically what sin did to a person spiritually. In examining a suspected case of leprosy, the priest was repeatedly warned to look below the skin. This depicts the **insidious** nature of sin: spreading from a small beginning to complete infection. God was the only source of healing for the disease of leprosy as He is for the sinful heart. It is interesting to note that the law instructed how to diagnose leprosy and shut the leper out from the congregation, but it had no power to heal him. No clearer proof of His divinity did Jesus give than His power to heal the lepers.

Contaminated Clothing and Homes

If we find anything in our lives that is displeasing to God through the searchlight of His Word or the diagnosis of His Spirit, we should not hesitate to remove it.

Instructions were given for identifying leprosy in clothing and houses. These have referred to a type of mildew in the case of fabric and dry-rot in the case of houses. Leprosy in houses would not be a consideration until they reached Canaan, since at this time they lived in tents. However, whatever looked like leprosy, whether fabric or wall, was to be destroyed. It should remind us that we cannot treat sin lightly. If we find anything in our lives that is displeasing to God through the searchlight of His Word or the diagnosis of His Spirit, we should not hesitate to remove it. Any attitude or habit that is displeasing to God must go. Self-examination is necessary for our spiritual as well as physical well-being.

Back to Normal

The purification of the leper had two distinct stages: (a) He was received back into the community of Israel; (b) He was fully reestablished in the favor and fellowship of God. Before these occurred, two living clean birds were to be brought and a specific ceremony performed. After completion of this ritual, the healed leper was allowed to return to the general community, but to return to worship, he had to do more. A week must pass and then the healed person had to bring a trespass offering, a sin offering, and a burnt offering, along with oil and grain, for the rituals necessary to return his privilege of public worship. Pictured through all these was the effectiveness of right sacrifice for the removal of the death sentence caused by sin and the restoration of physical and spiritual health. The blood was a token of forgiveness and the oil for healing, just as God first forgave our sins and then healed our diseases (Psalm 103:3; Isaiah 38:17).

"Cleanliness is Next to Godliness" This phrase is not a Bible verse, but it summarizes an important connection seen in Leviticus. Following the command to "be holy" were the laws requiring man to "be clean." Israel was to be clean in body, clothing, house, camp, in short, everywhere. In all the laws of Moses, the purity of the body was connected with the purity of the soul. *"Let us draw near with a true heart in full assurance of faith, having our hearts sprinkled from an evil conscience and our bodies washed with pure water"* (Hebrews 10:22). Inside and out, humanity needed cleaning. The book of Leviticus was like a mirror, revealing this on-going need.

"Let us draw near with a true heart in full assurance of faith, having our hearts sprinkled from an evil conscience and our bodies washed with pure water" (Hebrews 10:22).

The Day of Atonement Leviticus 16:1-34 Only one day a year could the High Priest enter the Holy of Holies. This was called the Day of Atonement and more than any other holy day, it pictured through its services and ceremonies what Christ would do as our High Priest.

The Ritual All the sacrifices on the Day of Atonement were performed by the High Priest himself. He first washed his body in the Holy Place and put on his white linen garments. Coming out of the tabernacle, he brought sacrifices for himself and his family—a young bull for a sin offering and a ram for a burnt offering. This part of the ceremony represented the imperfection of the Levitical priesthood. The High Priest then led forth the offerings for the people's sins—a ram for a burnt offering and two young goats for a sin offering. The two goats were presented before the Lord at the door of the tabernacle to have **lots** cast to determine which was the **scapegoat** and which the sacrifice. After the victims were prepared, the High Priest offered the young bull as a sin offering for himself and his family. Having slain it at the altar, he took some of its blood with a **censer** filled with live coals from the altar and a handful of incense. Entering into the Most Holy Place, he threw the incense on the coals, forming a cloud partially covering the ark, and then sprinkled the blood seven times before the mercy seat. The goat was then slain as a sin offering for the people, with the High Priest returning to the Most Holy Place to repeat the same ceremony with its blood. As he passed through the Holy Place, he purified it by sprinkling some of the blood of both victims on the altar of incense. This act completed the purification of the sanctuary.

lots - objects used (like dice) in determining a question by chance

scapegoat - a person or thing bearing the blame for others

censer - a vessel for burning incense

The Scapegoat

Next followed the significant ceremony of the scapegoat. The High Priest laid his hands on the head of the remaining goat and confessed over it the sins of the people. The goat, symbolically loaded with those sins, was led out by a man chosen for that purpose to the wilderness into *"an uninhabited land"* and there let loose. The meaning of this ritual was the complete removal of sins. What a lesson the scapegoat taught: It was led away, never to return, so that Israel could return to God, never to be led away. Christ bore our sins so that we could be free to return to God. Christ not only was our sin offering, paying the death penalty we should have paid, but also our scapegoat, removing our weight of sin so that we were freed to return to God.

Christ not only was our sin offering, paying the death penalty we should have paid, but also our scapegoat, removing our weight of sin so that we were freed to return to God.

Christ Our High Priest

Fulfilling the symbolism of the Day of Atonement, Jesus became our High Priest who laid aside the garments of royalty to humble Himself and become a man. Unlike any other High Priest, He did not have to bring sacrifices for Himself, because He never sinned. He was a High Priest so effective that He only had to offer Himself once to provide eternal removal of sin and reconciliation of man with God. The law required water, oil, and blood to ready a man for the job of High Priest. Jesus, not because of any sin of His own, but to *"fulfill all righteousness"* was baptized with water, anointed with the Holy Spirit, and made His own blood an offering to become our eternal and effective High Priest.

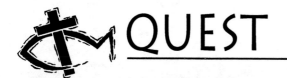

QUEST

Questions

Study Procedure: Read the Scripture references before answering questions. Unless otherwise instructed, use the Bible only in answering questions. Some questions may be more difficult than others but try to answer as many as you can. Pray for God's wisdom and understanding as you study and don't be discouraged if some answers are not obvious at first. Do not read the study notes for this lesson until AFTER you have completed your questions.

Day One: Vocabulary: Write the words that these definitions define.

1. _____ an act of removal of anything alien, improper, unnecessary, corrupting or otherwise damaging

2. _____ in a manner that can be heard

3. _____ developing so gradually as to be well established before becoming apparent

4. _____ a person or thing bearing the blame for others

5. _____ objects used (like dice) in determining a question by chance

6. _____ a vessel for burning incense

7. _____ living near or about the habitations of man

8. Did you have any additional thoughts on the Day of Atonement that you would like to share with the class? _____

_____

_____

_____

Day Two: Read Leviticus, Chapters 17-20   **MEMORY: LEVITICUS 19:18**

1. Leviticus 17 forbids some activities. Name them and give the reference. _____

_____

_____

_____

_____

2. What was the judgment for those who disobeyed God's command? _____

_____

_____

3. According to Leviticus 18:3, 19:2, and 20:23-24, why did God need to be so strict in his

   training with the children of Israel? _____

   _____

   _____

4. a) What is homosexuality as far as God is concerned according to Leviticus 18:22, Leviticus

      20:13 and Romans 1:21-28? _____

   b) Contrast this with present-day opinion. _____

      _____

      _____

Day Three:

MEMORY: MATTHEW 25:35-40

1. List the verses from Leviticus 19 that show
   concern for the poor and the stranger.

   _____

2. a) List the verses that show God's concern that the people be honest with God and their

      neighbors. _____

   b) What two physical handicaps are mentioned? _____

      _____

3. Read Leviticus 19:31 and Leviticus 20:6. Write down any present day activities that these might

   affect. _____

   _____

4. What verses in Leviticus Chapters 19 and 20 emphasize the fifth commandment?

   _____

Day Four: Read Leviticus 21-24

1. Listed below are the seven feasts given in Leviticus 23. Give the verses where they are found.

   a) The Feast of the Passover   _____

   b) The Feast of Unleavened Bread   _____

   c) The Feast of the Firstfruits   _____

   d) The Feast of Pentecost   _____

   e) The Feast of Trumpets _____

   f) The Feast of Atonement _____

   g) The Feast of Tabernacles   _____

Try to memorize the feasts.

2. Later, when Israel was settled in their own land, a Jewish person could make three trips to Jerusalem a year and celebrate all seven of these feasts.

Group them below.

a) Spring _____

b) Early Summer _____

c) Fall _____

_____

3. From Leviticus 24, what was the penalty for blasphemy? _____

Day Five: Read Leviticus, Chapters 25-27

MEMORY: ROMANS 13:8

Matching:

a) confess their sins

b) the sabbatic year

c) year of jubilee

d) obey all His laws

e) prices of property

f) relatives

g) failure to obey all God's laws

h) the land

_____1. Six years you shall sow, prune, and gather, but in this, the seventh year, it shall be a sabbath of rest unto the land.

_____2. This cannot be sold forever but is to be returned to the original owner every fifty years.

_____3. After 49 years, on the tenth day of the seventh month, the trumpet blows to start this special 50th year celebration.

_____4. Charge no interest to them when lending money.

_____5. If this is done, God promises appropriate rain, abundant crops, peace, and supernatural power.

_____6. If this happens, Israel will experience disease, oppression, poverty, insecurity, unanswered prayer, fear, and separation.

_____7. If this is done, God will remember His covenant with Israel's ancestors and remember the land.

_____8. More expensive the farther away from the Jubilee the date of purchase was.

9. Now take a few minutes to read your study notes for this lesson.

Notes

Fellowship Through Obedience

The spiritual parallel to this in Leviticus is that by accepting the sacrifice God has provided to pay for our sin, we are "born" into His family in a new, secure relationship.

When someone is born into a family, he is biologically or genetically always part of that family. However, if for some reason he is physically separated from that family through distance or through choosing to rebel against or ignore them with his behavior, he will not enjoy a close fellowship with that family. He will neither really know them, nor feel happily connected to them. The spiritual parallel to this in Leviticus is that by accepting the sacrifice God has provided to pay for our sin, we are "born" into His family in a new, secure relationship. However, if we want to really enjoy our place in His family, we must spend time with God, getting to know Him, and, because He is superior in every way, obeying His commands. Our relationship was secured by the blood of Jesus, but our fellowship is determined by our obedience to God's will. Continual obedience is possible only through faith in Christ's power to work in and through us. *"For it is God who works in you both to will and to do for His good pleasure"* (Philippians 2:13). Of course, He only tells us to do what is good, right, and helpful, so obeying Him makes us enjoy our relationship all the more.

Connecting Two Sections

Chapter 17 of Leviticus connects the two sections of Leviticus that explain these truths:

Section One: Chapters 1-16 How to Come Near to a Holy God (Relationship)
          The Tabernacle and its Sacrifices
Section Two: Chapters 17-27 How to Stay Near a Holy God (Fellowship)
          Laws to Obey

The Necessity of Blood

The key verse for understanding the need for sacrifice for sin is in Leviticus 17:11: *"For the life of the flesh is in the blood, and I have given it to you upon the altar to make atonement for your souls; for it is the blood that makes atonement for the soul."*

atonement - a covering for sin which makes reconciliation possible

No matter what we personally think about blood sacrifice, we have never been in the position to set the terms upon which we could be forgiven and restored to God. We must accept what God has said in His Word as the only way to be forgiven: *"...without shedding of blood there is no remission"* (Hebrews 9:22). God, who called us, also provided **atonement**, so that sinful men might approach the heavenly throne to find *"grace to help in time of need"* (Hebrews 4:16).

The Value of Obedience

God gave the blood to bring His people near, but He also provided a way for them to stay near in a continuing walk of fellowship with Him. The second section of Leviticus emphasized this truth. The ceremonies and rituals required of Israel can still teach Christians much about God's concept of separation or holy living. First Peter 1:14-16 says, *"as obedient children, not conforming yourselves to the former lusts, as in your ignorance; but as He who called you is holy, you also be holy in all your conduct, because it is written, 'Be holy, for I am holy.'"* Obedience to God's laws would keep Israel aware of and away from the unholy ways of heathen people surrounding them.

commonwealth - a nation, state, or other political unit

The Place of Sacrifice
Leviticus 17:1-9

God commanded that there should be one altar, one high priest, one sanctuary, and one body of people or **commonwealth** of Israel. Later, Israel sinned by "sacrificing in high places" and this deed resulted in **apostasy,** that had to be punished.

apostasy - revolt; renunciation of a religious faith

Sanctity of the Blood
Leviticus 17:10-16

God commanded that blood should not be eaten as food. Why? There are two reasons given. First, blood is the essential element of life: *"the life of the flesh is in the blood."* Medical science cannot manufacture blood in a laboratory or factory. Man can live with artificial hearts, limbs, and other things, but not without human blood. It cannot be man-made so it must be shared, given from one living person to another. Blood equals life. Secondly, man was not to eat blood because that would be treating it as something ordinary or common which it was not: *"It is the blood that makes atonement for the soul"* (Leviticus 17:11). It is interesting to note that the modern Jew does not practice the ritual of sacrifice but is still strict about the eating of blood. Blood is sacred as the symbol of life, and orthodox Jews eat only **kosher** meat, meat that is killed and prepared according to their requirements.

kosher - right, proper

Unlawful Marriages and Sexual Relations
Leviticus 18:1-30

"I am the Lord your God" was repeated six times in this chapter to give great seriousness to the requirements God issued here.

1. Unlawful Marriages: (Leviticus 18:1-19) In Genesis it was revealed that the human race came from a single pair, and, after the flood, the world was repopulated from one family. However, at the time of Leviticus, God determined it appropriate to have strict laws governing intermarriage, to counteract the evil influence on the family life and in interest of the society surrounding the children of Israel. No marriages or sexual relationships with close relatives were allowed.

2. Sexual Sins: (Leviticus 18:20-23) Unnatural lusts, sodomy and bestiality (unnatural sexual relationships with animals) were disgusting or abominable to God. Paul explained in Romans 1:24-27 that people get caught up in sexual misbehavior when God is not worshiped and obeyed:

"Therefore God also gave them up to uncleanness, in the lusts of their hearts, to dishonor their bodies among themselves, who exchanged the truth of God for the lie, and worshiped and served the creature rather than the Creator, who is blessed forever. Amen. For this reason God gave them up to vile passions. For even their women exchanged the natural use for what is against nature. Likewise also the men, leaving the natural use of the woman, burned in their lust for one another, men with men committing what is shameful, and receiving in themselves the penalty of their error which was due." Paul, in this passage, went on to say how they chose not to keep God in their hearts, and how He gave them over to a polluted mind to do these unnatural things that are not right. Without the revealed Word of God, society sickens and sinks into this low state. People make choices, and we can choose to call something acceptable when the Bible calls it otherwise, but not without consequences. God created humans as male and female; homosexuality mocks this difference and perverts the gift of sexual expression given to the marriage relationship. The Israelites were commanded over and over again to live pure and holy lives on the ground that God, the Holy One, was their God and that they were His people. In the New Testament, we are commanded to live obedient lives for the same reason: God, the Holy One, is our God and we are His people.

People make choices, and we can choose to call something acceptable when the Bible calls it otherwise, but not without consequences.

Summary
Leviticus 18:24-30

God made us for His glory. Obedience to God brings the greatest joy and satisfaction, while disobedience pushes us into the conditions of misery and perversion. Each sin has the potential for taking the sinner down the awful path away from God. Only God's Holy Spirit can keep us from sin. We must make a personal choice to follow Him.

Only God's Holy Spirit can keep us from sin.

Basic Morality Parenting
Leviticus 19:1-37

Several of the Ten Commandments were repeated here. Interestingly the first one was to honor or **revere** mother and father. Without respect for parents there could be no enduring social order, and without such respect there was likely to be little regard for or understanding of God. Honor for parents and respect for authority has to be taught to children individually, repeatedly and consistently, or they enter society without proper respect for or submission to those over them in school, business, or government. The greatest problems in our society could be corrected if parents would return to Scriptural parenting,

revere - to show devotion and honor to

properly training their own children according to godly principles. The baby-sitter, school, church, youth group, civic club, military unit, or police force cannot fill the role God gave to parents.

Worship

To remain separate from the heathen people already inhabiting Canaan, Israel was commanded to make no idols and to keep the Sabbaths according to God's instructions.

God's Welfare System

Recognizing the on-going problem of the poor needing food, God made provision for gleaning. When the Jew and Gentile became landowners in Israel, they were not to harvest the corners of their grain fields or pick up what might fall from the harvesters' sacks or carts. They were not to strip every grape from their grape vines but purposely leave some for the poor to gather or glean. God is still concerned about the poor and expects us to find ways to help them.

God Really Cares

Covered in the remaining verses were warnings against withholding someone's wages, hurting the handicapped, gossiping, farming improperly, abusing one's body with cuttings or tattoos, giving attention to any occult practices, dishonoring the elderly, abusing strangers, or being dishonest in business.

Penalties for Lawbreakers
Leviticus 20

The death penalty was to be given to those worshiping Molech, a god of the Phoenicians whose worship involved child sacrifice, sexual deviations, and witchcraft. A person turning to a **medium** or seeking **familiar spirits** would be cut off from Israel. America's obsession with Halloween, daily horoscopes and psychics should be examined in light of God's clear law against witchcraft. To endorse even casually, through only occasional participation, the working of a power in opposition to God is idolatry.

> **medium** - an individual held to be a channel of communication between the earthly world and the world of spirits

> **familiar spirits** - spirits or demons that serve or prompt an individual

Proper Priests and Perfect Sacrifices
Leviticus 21 and 22

Since the priests were called to the highest possible service, they had to abide by strict regulations for behavior and appearance. God gave restrictions for whom they were to marry, and God issued a standard of physical health by which active priests were to be measured. In Chapter 22 a warning was issued about trying to offer imperfect animals as sacrifices. God knew the heart of man very well!

The Seven Feasts of Israel
Leviticus 23

Besides a weekly sabbath observance that required a stopping of all work, God issued orders for seven more special assemblies throughout the year that could be observed in three trips to the national place of worship.

Spring

Passover was to be on the 14th day of the first month of spring and followed by a seven-day feast called Unleavened Bread, which began on the 15th. On the day after the Sabbath that would fall during the seven days following Passover, the people were to thank God by presenting a sheaf of their **firstfruits** and sacrificing a lamb before Him. This offering was called the Feast of Firstfruits.

firstfruits - a sample of the first crops to ripen

Early Summer

After returning from the spring trip and proceeding with the farming duties, the people were to count fifty days after Firstfruits and return to offer God a new grain offering and additional animal sacrifices. This feast was called the Feast of Weeks, since it occurred seven weeks after Firstfruits and later was called Pentecost, meaning fifty days.

Fall Trip

On the first day of the seventh month there was to be a blowing of trumpets signalling the end of the harvest period and a time to regather for worship. This time was called the Feast of Trumpets (Rosh Hashanah) and required a sacrifice by fire to the Lord. On the tenth day of that same month was the Day of Atonement or Yom Kippur, the most solemn and holy of all the special days. This was the one day of the whole year when the High Priest was able to enter the Holy of Holies to offer sacrifice for himself and the nation to have their sins covered for another year. It is still traditionally a day of fasting and repentance for the religious Jew. On the fifteenth day of the seventh month, the Feast of Tabernacles began and lasted for seven days. It was like an outdoor community camp-out where families built temporary dwellings from sticks and brush to commemorate their deliverance from Egypt and God's provision for them in the wilderness. That week ended with an eighth day of Sabbath rest.

This was the one day of the whole year when the High Priest was able to enter the Holy of Holies to offer sacrifice for himself and the nation to have their sins covered for another year.

Lamps, Bread, Eyes, and Teeth
Leviticus 24

More directions are given in this chapter for the proper method for making the oil for the tabernacle and the baking and placement of the showbread. The chapter ends with the tragic account of a young man from a mixed marriage being sentenced to stoning for cursing God. Also in this chapter was found the famous "eye for an eye" ruling, which actually promoted mercy and balance in acts of retaliation for crimes, in marked contrast to the practice of heathen cultures, which showed no limits in avenging themselves on their enemies.

The Sabbatical Year and the Year of Jubilee
Leviticus 25:1-55

The Sabbatical year and the year of Jubilee (from *jubal*: to blow a trumpet) had significance throughout Scripture in the religious observance of the law. The sacred observances of Israel are arranged in cycles of seven, the number for completeness or perfection. First, there was a cycle of seven days, ending with the Sabbath. Second, was a cycle of seven weeks, closing with the Feast of Weeks. Third, was a cycle of seven months, ending with the "Month of Feasts," and fourth, was a cycle of seven years, and fifth, was a cycle of seven weeks (seven "sevens") of years, followed by the Jubilee.

Sabbaths and Sabbaticals

The seventh day in every week was set apart as a day in which no work was to be done. The seventh year was set apart as a year in which no seed was to be sown. At the end of seven times seven or 49 years, there was a great festival during which the whole land was to rest, when debts were to be cancelled, property returned to owners, and slaves to be set free. God had every right to require these "sabbaths" because He owned everything, and the people of Israel were merely managers or **stewards** for Him. This is also true of us today. If these regular rests for the land, people, and debts were observed, the land would benefit ecologically, the people would benefit socially and spiritually, and the economic structure of the nation would be balanced, without great divisions continuing between rich and poor.

> **stewards** - ones who manage money or property for another

> *At the end of seven times seven or 49 years, there was a great festival during which the whole land was to rest, when debts were to be cancelled, property returned to owners, and slaves to be set free.*

The Sabbatical Year
Leviticus 25:1-7

The celebration of this special year was represented as a period of rest for the land. The people did not plant, prune, or gather during this year. Along with the command to celebrate the Sabbath, or sabbatical year, came the promise that there would be plenty from the sixth year to sustain them, not only during the seventh year, but also through the eighth year, as they planted and pruned until they could harvest in the ninth year. Keeping this law required faith and obedience.

The Year of Jubilee
Leviticus 25:8-55

This year was an intensified form of the sabbatical year and came after seven weeks (or seven "sevens") of years. It also was rest for the land and a year of liberty: a returning of possessions to original owners and a return of separated members to their families. The amount of time remaining before the next Jubilee had to be considered in buying or selling land, lending money, or any other financial dealing.

Jesus in Jubilee

Jesus chose the words of Isaiah which expressed the spiritual meaning of the year of Jubilee for His first public speech because He came to provide the blessings of Jubilee: *"The Spirit of the Lord God is upon Me, because the Lord has anointed Me to preach good tidings to the poor; He has sent Me to heal the brokenhearted, to proclaim liberty to the captives, and the opening of the prison to those who are bound; to proclaim the acceptable year of the Lord..."* (Isaiah 61:1,2 and Luke 4:18,19).

Final Appeal
Leviticus 26:1-46

The code of holiness in the book of Leviticus concluded in this 26th chapter with promises of blessings for obedience but definite punishments for disobedience. These were expressed in traditional covenant language, making clear to all involved what was expected. The list of what God wanted to do for them if they would obey Him was spectacular—how could they not obey when so much depended on it? Yet, how can we not obey when we are promised so many of the same blessings?

Voluntary Devotion
Leviticus 27:1-34

The book of Leviticus ends with supplemental teaching regarding vows or pledges of extra acts of obedience not normally required by the law. When a vow was voluntarily made to God, He expected it to be kept. In every group of God's people, there are those who want to do more than usual for God. God accepts such second-mile service when it is offered with sincerity and humility.

Last Word on Leviticus

This has been a short study of this important book. Leviticus showed us that the proper approach to God was through sacrifice and the way to maintain a closeness was through obedience. As Christians we recognize Christ as the complete and eternal sacrifice who brings us near to God. We also recognize His Holy Spirit living in us after our conversion as the power keeping us close to God and enabling us to obey His Word. To study the book of Leviticus properly, we would need a full year. However, in this overview it is hoped that personal study time, class discussion, and these notes have given you a basic understanding of the truths expressed in this book which has been so rich in God's picture-language.

As Christians we recognize Christ as the complete and eternal sacrifice who brings us near to God and His Holy Spirit living in us after our conversion as the power keeping us close to God and enabling us to obey His Word.

Review

Christ fulfilled the teaching of Leviticus: He brought us near to God through His blood sacrifice and empowers us to enjoy that nearness through obedience to God's will. Further, Christ's sacrifice was illustrated in all five of the required tabernacle offerings, and His ministry and gifts were foreshadowed in the detailed description of the anointed High Priest. The furniture of the tabernacle dramatized the results of His crucifixion, resurrection, and ascension. Finally, the seven feasts, were used by Jesus in the New Testament as divine appointments to be kept and fulfilled. He was crucified on Passover as the Lamb of God, buried without sin on the Feast of Unleavened Bread, and raised from the dead as the *"firstfruits of those who have fallen asleep"* on the Feast of Firstfruits. Fifty days later He fulfilled His promise and poured out the Holy Spirit on the Feast of Pentecost, resulting in an initial "harvest" of 3000 people. We wait eagerly for Christ to come in fulfillment of the final three: The Feast of Trumpets: perhaps to call the church home before returning to earth with them for the fulfillment of the end-time prophecies; The Day of Atonement: Christ's return to earth, when in fulfillment of Zechariah 12:10 all of Israel will mourn for Him, *"and look on Me Whom they have pierced"*; and finally, the Feast of Tabernacles: perhaps to reign over the earth as its perfect **Sovereign** for a thousand years. It is hoped that Leviticus has proved to be a key book for understanding the Scriptures, especially those pertaining to the saving work of Christ. He brought us into God's family and empowers us to enjoy the rich benefits of our inheritance.

> **Sovereign** - King; one who has supreme power or authority

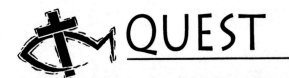 QUEST

Questions

Study Procedure: Read the Scripture references before answering questions. Unless otherwise instructed, use the Bible only in answering questions. Some questions may be more difficult than others but try to answer as many as you can. Pray for God's wisdom and understanding as you study and don't be discouraged if some answers are not obvious at first. Do not read the study notes for this lesson until AFTER you have completed your questions.

Day One: Vocabulary Review

1. A nation, state, or other political unit is called a _____.

2. A revolt against or a renunciation of a religious faith is called _____.

3. To cover sin so that reconciliation can occur is to make an _____.

4. In Hebrew, if something is right or proper it is _____.

5. To show devotion and honor to something or someone is to _____ it.

6. In the practice of the occult, the individual held to be a channel of communication between the earthly world and the world of spirits is called a _____.

7. _____ are spirits or demons that serve or prompt an individual.

8. A sample of the first crops to ripen offered to God in gratitude were _____.

9. Someone who manages the property for another is called a _____.

10. One who has supreme power or authority is _____.

11. Name one or two subjects from last week's Scripture or the summary given in the notes about which you feel that Christians today should be more concerned . _____

_____

_____

_____

Day Two: Read Numbers 1-4

MEMORY: ROMANS 4:7-8

1. a) Make a list of the sons of Jacob, including the two sons of Joseph, from Numbers 1:1-15. _____

_____

_____

b) Compare this list with Genesis 35:23-26. Which name is missing in the list in Numbers?

_____

c) Give the reason for this from Numbers 1. (Give verses.) _____

_____

_____

_____

2. The book of Leviticus was a manual of worship for the children of Israel. What phrase in the first chapter of Numbers would be a key as to what confronts the children of Israel in the book of Numbers? _____

3. In the notes for Lesson 16, take time to study the chart on the tabernacle, in the section named "Camp Organization." Note carefully the positions of the tribes. Becoming familiar with this will help in the remaining lessons through Joshua. What was central in the camp? _____

4. a) Fill in the number given for each tribe of men that were twenty years old and above.

   Reuben_____   Judah _____   Simeon   _____

   Issachar   _____   Gad_____   Zebulun _____

   Ephraim   _____   Manasseh _____   Benjamin_____

   Dan   _____   Asher _____   Naphtali _____

   b) How many men were there? _____

5. Comment on the careful record of names and numbers in Chapters 3 and 4. What do you find encouraging when you think about your own service for God today? _____

   _____

   _____

   _____

Day Three: Read Numbers 5   *MEMORY: NUMBERS 6:24-26*

1. What three kinds of defilement are mentioned
   in Numbers 5:1-4? _____

   _____

2. Describe the unique "lie detector" test used in Numbers 5: 11-31._____

   _____

   _____

   _____

3. Read Numbers 6. Summarize the requirements for fulfilling a Nazarite vow.

   a) Cannot drink or eat_____

   b) Cannot cut _____

   c) Cannot go near a _____

4. What was the purpose of the Nazarite vow? _____

   _____

119

5. From your dictionary or handbook on the Bible, give the names of some men who were apparently under a Nazarite vow. _____

Day Four: Read Numbers 7-9   *MEMORY: JEREMIAH 9:23-24*

1. The seventh chapter of Numbers has much repetition, but in spite of this, what do you find most interesting? _____

_____

_____

2. a) From Chapter 8 give the verse that explains why God calls the **Levites** a "gift to Aaron."

_____

b) Between what ages were the Levites allowed to serve?_____

3. In Numbers 9, what guided the movements of this huge group of **people?** _____

_____

4. What do you think would have been the results had the children of Israel just ignored this means of guidance? _____

_____

_____

_____

5. How should we determine God's guidance for us today? _____

_____

_____

Day Five: Read Numbers 10

1. What are the purposes given here for the sounding of trumpets? _____

_____

_____

2. When did the journey of the children of Israel begin again? _____

_____

3. How did they know it was time to move? _____

_____

4. What did Moses say when the ark set out and when it rested? _____

_____

_____

_____

5. Now take a few minutes to read your study notes for this lesson.

Notes

Ready to Go!

The title for Numbers in Greek is *"arithmoi,"* related to our "arithmetic" and means "counting" or "numbering." Numbers is the fourth of the first five Bible books that Moses authored and begins and ends with two big countings: Chapter 1 is a census of the people in the second year after leaving Egypt, and Chapter 26 recounts them after forty years in the wilderness. The population count or **census** of Israel was made for these reasons:

census - a count of the population

1. Proof: How amazing that God's power was so great that He could free, feed, organize, and guide a nation whose able-bodied male members over age twenty numbered 603,550. That made the total population somewhere between two and three million! This numbering was proof of God's blessing on them.

2. Provision: Counts were taken for future use in figuring provisions for food, camping space, and military efforts. God, of course, did not need the figures, but His human organizers attempting to carry out His will would.

3. Placement: When they finally arrived in the Promised Land the families who had been carefully registered in the census would be placed on their own land.

How amazing that God's power was so great that He could free, feed, organize, and guide a nation whose able-bodied male members over age twenty numbered 603,550. That made the total population somewhere between two and three million!

Three Sections We will survey this book with its many interesting details about the forty years in the wilderness in three divisions:
1) Israel's Preparation for the Journey (Numbers 1:1-10:10)
2) Journey from Sinai to Kadesh (Numbers 10:11-21:35)
3) Journey from Kadesh to Moab (Numbers 22:1-36:13)

The First Census
Numbers 1:1-54

It had been one month since the completion of the tabernacle (compare Numbers 1:1 with Exodus 40:17), and Moses had plenty to oversee with the new worship schedule and the daily responsibilities of being the leader of two or three million ex-slaves in the middle of a desert. But God gave Moses another assignment: to count all the people. Amazingly, to anyone in

procrastinate - to put off intentionally something that should be done now

exempt - free or released from some duty to which others are subject

standard - a conspicuous object, used at the top of a pole, to mark a rallying point, especially in battle

Interestingly, God still does not require everyone to be just alike but does desire unity in our diversity.

leadership, Moses did not **procrastinate** but started the process the very same day. The goal of the census was to register from each tribe the able-bodied men over twenty who could go to war. It was time to go and claim the land God had promised, but it would take many battles to clear the present inhabitants away. God said He would judge the people of the land of Canaan (the Amorites) for their wickedness. Israel was to execute this action in the name and by the command of God. The tribe of Levi was **exempt** from the military duties. God had reversed the curse that Jacob put on that tribe years before and blessed them for their zeal for His honor in the incident of the golden calf. The Levites were set apart from the rest of the tribes for the service of the sanctuary. (Read Exodus 32:26.) When Levi was set apart, it might appear that there would be only eleven tribes left to serve, but actually there were twelve even without Levi. Back in Genesis, Jacob was so thrilled with Joseph's rise to power and their reunion that he gave Joseph a double inheritance. So, instead of Joseph's name being listed in the twelve, his sons Ephraim and Manasseh would appear, making thirteen tribes. With Levi set apart for special duties now, the number returned to twelve.

Camp Organization
Numbers 2:1-4:49

After Moses and the assistants God had named from each tribe finished the count, the Lord gave them another order. They were to position the tribes around the tabernacle in a specified order with each tribe camping around its own **standard**, and each family around its own emblem. Interestingly, God still does not require everyone to be just alike but does desire unity in our diversity. The general camp was to be in the form of a square with each side given to three tribes that were closest in hereditary relationship to each other. (See illustration below.) God assigned the positions, not Moses, perhaps to avoid any strife or envy among the tribes.

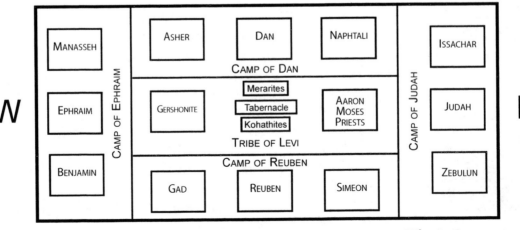

The Camp

Marching Orders Whenever the camp moved, Judah, Issachar, and Zebulun, who camped on the east with 186,400 soldiers, led the way. Immediately after these were two families of Levites, the Gershonites and the Merarites, with 13,700 men who were responsible for carrying the furniture of the tabernacle on wagons. Next, the south side made up of Reuben, Simeon, and Gad with their army of 151,450 followed. Behind these another family of Levites, the Kohathites, with 8,600 men were in charge of the sanctuary. Ephraim leading Manasseh and Benjamin on the west side with a total of 108,100 fighting men were followed by the northern camp of Dan, Asher, and Naphtali, with 157,600 warriors, who brought up the rear. The families were kept together in each tribe. What a sight this must have been!

Special Duties
Numbers 3:1-4:49 The Levites had charge of the tabernacle and carried it. The assignments were clearly given and the individual responsibilities were taken seriously. Learning how important it is for each one to do his part is a valuable lesson in our work for God, too. Moving such a huge number of people would have been impossible without individuals being clearly organized and faithful to their particular assignments. Nothing is insignificant when done for God.

Interesting Arithmetic God had Moses count all the male Levites over one month old; they totaled 22,000. God also had Moses count all the male children in Israel over one month old who were the first to be born in their families. This census totalled 22,273. God said that since by His power those firstborn had been spared the death blow received by the other firstborn back in Egypt, they technically belonged to Him. Instead of having the firstborn of every individual family sent to the tabernacle to serve, however, God accepted the 22,000 male Levites in their place. Interestingly, because every single life was significant to God, He would not "round off" the difference of 273 but had them "redeemed" by paying five shekels each to Aaron and his sons for the work of the the sanctuary. Our God is so consistent and careful! No life is unimportant to Him.

More "Colorful" Details Chapter 4 gave the instructions for packing and carrying the contents of the tabernacle. From past lessons the symbolism returned: blue for the Holy Spirit or heavenly association; scarlet for sacrificial blood; badger skins, probably dark or dull in color, hiding from the world the true beauty underneath; and purple, symbolic of royalty or divinity.

Personal Problems

Separation
Numbers 5:1-4

These regulations would be constant reminders of God's concern for maintaining clean, healthy bodies as well as pure hearts.

Whether on the march or in camp, the people were to observe the purification laws. Lepers, people with bodily discharges, or persons having had contact with a corpse were to be put outside the normal camp boundaries. These regulations would be constant reminders of God's concern for maintaining clean, healthy bodies as well as pure hearts.

Restitution
Numbers 5:5-10

If another person was wronged, restitution was to be made. In Numbers 5:7, twenty percent extra was to be given in addition to what was repaid, most probably to help soothe the strained situation. Zacchaeus, in Luke 19:8, showed the changing power of Christ in his life when he pledged four hundred percent restitution to all those he had wronged. We need to consider the appropriateness of restitution in our own relationships.

Lie-Detector Test?
Numbers 5:11-31

Adultery was forbidden in the Ten Commandments and the odd procedure described here was intended to reveal the truth when adultery was suspected by a husband about his wife. Sexual faithfulness between husband and wife was to be like a model to society of the faithfulness individuals were to have toward their true God. Violations of the marriage relationship were taken very seriously.

The Nazarite Vow
Numbers 6:1-22

Persons sometimes wanted to do something special to show their devotion to God. One experience they could choose was to make a vow to live differently or separately for a designated period. The Nazarite vow included abstaining from anything made with grapes, not cutting the hair, and not touching a corpse. A Nazarite was to be a living example of holiness, completely devoted to the Lord. Interestingly, nothing in this vow required one to remain unmarried. The things asked of a Nazarite could be done in regular family life.

So That's Where That Came From!
Numbers 6:22-27

countenance - appearance or expression seeming to approve or encourage

A most wonderful benediction was given in this chapter. Every heart can repeat it, every day and every night. How great the blessing of having God watch over us, giving us grace and peace. God so wanted to love and be loved by His people. *"The Lord bless you and keep you; the Lord make His face shine upon you, and be gracious to you; the Lord lift up His **countenance** upon you, and give you peace."*

A Long, Long List
Numbers 7:1-89

This was the longest chapter in Numbers and had to do with the princes of Israel bringing their offerings in covered wagons drawn by oxen. Every offering was carefully noted. To the reader it might seem repetitious, even boring, but the careful recording indicated that God cared about every single gift from every single giver. God does not forget anything that anyone does in His Name.

Dedicating the Levites
Numbers 8:1-26

A few more details were covered by God here: the correct arrangement of lamps in the tabernacle and the dedication ceremony of the Levites. They were given a twenty-five-year span of service, from age 25 to 50.

Time for Passover
Numbers 9:1-14

God commanded His people to keep the Passover, and they did so before leaving Sinai on their journey. He repeated some of the details for its correct observance and made allowances for a later celebration in exceptional situations.

The Cloud and Fire
Numbers 9:15-23

They were now ready to march toward the land of Canaan. Their movement would be guided entirely by the cloud which rested upon the tabernacle. If you skimmed this passage about the cloud, take time to re-read it carefully, letting yourself feel the powerful repetition of *"when the cloud remained"* and *"when the cloud continued."* What a lesson for us if we could learn only to move or stay where the Holy Spirit was leading us in our daily march! Can you imagine the discipline that was learned in obeying God's sovereign leading?

Have Trumpets, Will Travel
Numbers 10:1-10

Moses was commanded to make two silver trumpets to be used for calling the people together and as a signal for marching. Trumpets are prominent throughout Scripture as real attention-getters for significant actions. We will see them often in Israel's history. With everything in order, the people organized and the tabernacle packed, Israel was ready to move away from Sinai, with all they had learned there, and march toward their new land.

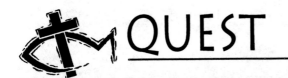 QUEST

Questions

Study Procedure: Read the Scripture references before answering questions. Unless otherwise instructed, use the Bible only in answering questions. Some questions may be more difficult than others but try to answer as many as you can. Pray for God's wisdom and understanding as you study and don't be discouraged if some answers are not obvious at first. Do not read the study notes for this lesson until AFTER you have completed your questions.

Day One: Vocabulary Review: Fill in the blanks with the vocabulary words in your notes

1. Moses did not _____ when God told him to conduct a _____
   of the able-bodied men over twenty.

2. Each tribe had its own _____ which could be seen from a distance and
   served as a gathering spot for the group.

3. The Levites were _____ from military service.

4. The face of God that looks favorably on His people is called His _____.

Read Numbers 10:11-36 and Judges 1:16 and 4:11

5. a) What reasons did Moses give his brother-in-law to persuade him to stay with them?

   _____

   _____

   _____

   _____

   b) Read Judges 1:16 and 4:11. What lesson can we learn from Moses' request of Hobab to stay?

   _____

   _____

   _____

   _____

   _____

Day Two: Read Numbers 11-12

MEMORY: JEREMIAH 29:12-13

1. From past lessons, list some of the
   miraculous signs of God's power and provision that Israel had seen up to this time.

   _____

   _____

   _____

MAP STUDY

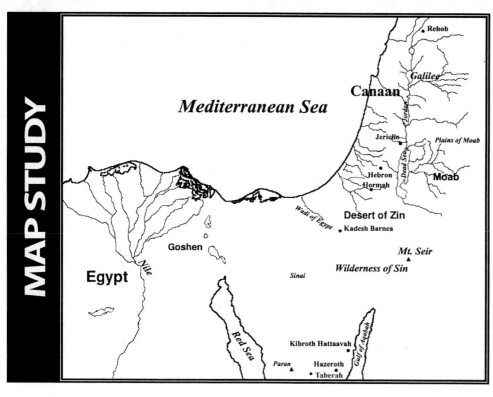

2. Map Work: Try to become familiar with this map as it will be important to a better understanding of the chapters we will be studying. As you read the chapters in this lesson, highlight with colored pencils the places mentioned in the journey of the children of Israel.

3. From Numbers 11, outline the action:

a) The people _____

b) The Lord _____

c) The people _____

d) Moses _____

e) The mixed multitude _____

_____

_____

f) Moses heard the weeping; the anger of the Lord was aroused; then, Moses was displeased and prayed _____

_____

_____

_____

g) God responded to Moses' prayer with this solution: _____

_____

_____

_____

4. Summarize from Numbers 12 the cause and cure of this sibling rivalry episode.

    _____

    _____

    _____

    _____

    _____

    _____

    _____

    _____

5. Supply the name of the speaker for each quotation:

    a) *"Are you zealous for my sake? Oh, that all the Lord's people were prophets..."*

    _____

    b) *"Has the Lord's arm been shortened?"* _____

    c) *"Has the Lord indeed spoken only through Moses?"* _____

    d) *"Did I conceive all these people?"* _____

    e) *"If her father had but spit in her face, would she not be shamed seven days?"*

    _____

    f) *"Why then were you not afraid to speak against My servant Moses?"* _____

    g) *"Give us meat, that we may eat."* _____

    h) *"Shall all the fish of the sea be gathered together for them...?"* _____

    i) *"Please do not let her be as one dead."* _____

Day Three: Read Numbers 13 and 14   **MEMORY: JEREMIAH 31:33**

1. From Kadesh, Moses sent men into Canaan to

    spy out the land. List some things for which Moses particularly asked them to look.

    _____

    _____

2. There were conflicting reports given about the twelve spies' forty-day tour.

    a) Summarize the majority report: _____

    _____

    b) Summarize the minority report: _____

    _____

3. From Numbers 14:1-12, summarize how the following responded to the reports:

    a) the people _____

    _____

    b) Moses and Aaron _____

    c) Joshua and Caleb _____

    _____

    d) the people again _____

    e) the Lord _____

    _____

4. On what grounds did Moses appeal to God for mercy? _____

    _____

    _____

    _____

    _____

5. How did God respond? _____

    _____

    _____

    _____

6. What foolish thing did Israel try at the end of Chapter 14? Comment on this._____

    _____

    _____

    _____

Day Four: Read Numbers 15, 16, and 17

1. From Numbers 15, give the significance for tassels on the men's garments._____

    _____

    _____

    _____

    _____

2. In Numbers 16 we have the sin of Korah, who led the rebellion to do away with the priesthood. How serious a matter was this with Korah and the 250 men who followed him, as well as the Israelites who were in sympathy with Korah? _____

    _____

3. What may we conclude from this about those who rebel against God-given authority?

    _____

4. By what sign, in Numbers 17, did God settle the question of the priesthood? _____

_____

_____

_____

_____

Day Five: Read Numbers 18-21   *MEMORY: LAMENTATIONS 3:22-23*

1. How did God provide for the financial
   upkeep of the priesthood and the needs of the _____
   tabernacle services? (Numbers 18) _____

_____

2. Chapter 19 gives instructions for being cleansed after touching **a dead body.** The ashes of a
   red heifer were to be kept on hand, ready to be sprinkled in the **water of** purification. Why would
   they need this supply at this time in their history? _____

_____

_____

_____

_____

3. Whose deaths are recorded in Numbers 20? _____

4. What was the sin of Moses? (Numbers 20:7-12) _____

_____

_____

_____

_____

5. What old enemy of Israel surfaced here? _____

6. In Numbers 21, what remedy did God provide for the sinful, snakebitten, rebellious Israelites
   which was used in the New Testament as a type of Christ and as a remedy for man today?
   (Read John 3:14-16.) _____

_____

_____

_____

7. Now take a few minutes to read your study notes for this lesson.

Notes

From Sinai to Kadesh

Review Exodus and Leviticus chronicled the first six-week march to Mount Sinai from Egypt and recorded the laws given during the remaining months of Israel's first year of freedom. Numbers began narrating the next forty years' action, beginning after the month-long celebration of the finished tabernacle, which was consecrated on the first day of the first month of the second year. Last week's lesson began with Moses counting the people on the first day of the second month and ended with the organized Israelites and their armies setting out on the twentieth day of the second month of the second year. The cloud moved, the trumpets sounded, and east, south, west, and north, the tribes joined ranks to follow. It should have taken eleven days to get to Canaan and start their new life. But that is not what happened.

It should have taken eleven days to get to Canaan and start their new life. But that is not what happened.

Hobab's Human Help Sought
Numbers 10:11-32 A personal incident in Moses' life was recorded here. Hobab, a relative by marriage, was preparing to leave Moses now, perhaps having stayed with him since the incident in Exodus 18. Moses asked him to stay because his knowledge of the area would be so helpful in their travels. According to Judges 1:16, 4:11 and 1 Samuel 15:6, Hobab accepted and received a settlement with them in the land of Canaan. With God's miraculous guidance ever before them, did Moses sin in asking Hobab to stay? There was nothing negative recorded resulting from this, so it would seem that using common sense along with the guidance of God's Holy Spirit was and is acceptable, so long as that common sense does not contradict God's clear commands. Being a Midianite and reared in that country, Hobab, no doubt, proved to be valuable to the Israelites. The pillar of cloud gave the general direction and kept before the people God's divine guidance. Hobab probably helped locate water, fuel, and pasture and warned them of the dangers of the desert. It would seem that God had prepared such a man as Hobab to go with Moses. He had been at Sinai, heard the law given, and knew it was God who was leading the children of Israel to the land of promise.

Guidance Today Instead of the outward pillar of cloud, we have an inward witness of the Holy Spirit when we have received Christ by faith. The inward voice of the Spirit should always be balanced with Scriptural truth. When those agree, then common sense, or a lining up of circumstances, gives a third witness that God is guiding us. Trusting human help alone is never wise, but when we are sure of God's inward voice and are in harmony with His revealed truth, human aid can be encouraging and useful.

131

The epistle writer James described the wisdom of God as contrasted with our own: *"For where envy and self-seeking exist, confusion and every evil thing are there. But the wisdom that is from above is first pure, then peaceable, gentle, willing to yield, full of mercy and good fruits, without partiality and without hypocrisy"* (James 3:16,17).

Paran
Numbers 10:33-36

The cloud led them three days away from Mount Sinai to their first resting place at Paran. The ark was at the front of the procession as a symbol of God's guidance in their journey. The remainder of the sacred vessels followed in the prescribed order.

Trouble at the Start
Numbers 11:1-3

In their first year there had been murmurings and unbelief, but God had not yet expressed His will through the law or revealed His glory during their worship. But on this side of Sinai, after a full year of evidence of God's loving provision and power, their murmuring brought quick **rebuke**. God sent holy fire down on them and burned many in judgment so that the place was called Taberah or "burning." The people cried to Moses; he quickly prayed to God, and the fire was quenched.

rebuke - to criticize sharply

Trouble Continued
Numbers 11:4-9

As we learned from our study in Exodus, not all the people who came out of Egypt were Hebrews (Exodus 12:38). There was a group which the Bible called a "mixed multitude," who probably were made up of non-Jews connected through marriage or friendship. This mixed group took the lead in murmuring against God's daily menu of manna. They were people with mixed interests. They perhaps wanted to be under the blessing of God's people but could not forget the pleasures of Egypt. Many people in the church today have mixed interests. They want to be Christian enough to experience **material** blessing and community respect, but they find no satisfaction in spiritual food. It has been said that it took God one night to get Israel out of Egypt, but forty years to get Egypt out of Israel. How much of Egypt does your church still contain? How mixed are the motives of your fellow members or yourself? If the complaining and murmuring are more common than prayer and thanksgiving, then we may be held back from receiving all the blessings God had planned for us and, instead, face some divine discipline.

material - concerned with physical rather than spiritual or intellectual things

It has been said that it took God one night to get Israel out of Egypt, but forty years to get Egypt out of Israel.

Moses Gets Discouraged
Numbers 11:10-30

To murmur against God after all His wonderful help was completely disrespectful, and Moses was extremely displeased with these people. His prayer in response to this should not necessarily be a model for us, but it did honestly express his overwhelming feelings of discouragement as the chosen leader of such an ungrateful people. He wanted to die if it was going to be so difficult. God did not reprimand Moses for his self-pity but focused instead on Moses' real need, promising him seventy elders to help him in leadership. Discouragement is still Satan's most crippling weapon against Christians. Who among us has not experienced its effects? The most mature Christian will fail at times, but God will hear our prayers for help. Instead of murmuring or moping, tell it all to God in prayer. He still understands and will give help. God wants us to keep a right attitude even when circumstances overwhelm us. Attitude is the only thing over which we always have control. Faith empowers us to keep our inner man holy, trusting God for the help we need elsewhere.

A Big Promise
Numbers 11:18-23

God further promised a month's supply of meat. Moses' response seemed dangerously disrespectful and doubting when he asked God if all the flocks were to be slaughtered and all the fish in the sea gathered to accomplish such a bold promise. God silenced Moses with a piercing response to his whining: *"Has the Lord's arm been shortened?"* When would he—when will we—see that nothing is impossible with God?

God silenced Moses with a piercing response to his whining: "Has the Lord's arm been shortened?"

Holy Spirit Shared
Numbers 11:24-30

God backed up Moses' authority by personally revealing Himself in the cloud when the seventy elders had been called. They received the Holy Spirit's power as Moses had and gave evidence of their new power by prophesying. Two men did not assemble with the others as called, but the Holy Spirit came on them where they were in the camp, causing them to prophesy, too. Joshua felt that they were out of order and wanted Moses to stop them, but Moses' response was precious and showed that he never wished to be the only one with special blessings from God. He said, *"Oh, that all the Lord's people were prophets and that the Lord would put His Spirit upon them!"* God would answer that desire many years later at a celebration of Pentecost when the Holy Spirit was loosed to be received by all who would receive Him.

Too Much of a Good Thing
Numbers 11:31-35

God gave a promise and a warning to Moses and the Israelites before sending quail to them after their murmuring. The wind brought them up from the sea, kept them close to the ground, and they were thick around the camp. Their greed for more than they needed was recorded here. They had hardly tasted the meat when a plague began among them. God *"gave them their request, but sent leanness into their soul"* (Psalm 106:15). It is important to see that the sin for which the people were punished was deeper than a complaining spirit or the sin of an uncontrolled physical appetite. The

craving - intense desire, deep yearning

real sin was the sin of unbelief. They did not think God could really satisfy them. The place was renamed Kibroth-hattaavah, "the graves of **craving**," as a shameful reminder of their behavior.

Sibling Rivalry
Numbers 12:1-16

Up to this point, only positive things had been recorded about Moses' older sister Miriam. She had bravely and cleverly acted in his behalf when he was found by the Pharaoh's daughter and saved from death, and she had led the women in singing and worship after God brought them through the Red Sea. Aaron, on the other hand, had had some bad moments in Scripture already, but both had a hidden sin: jealousy of their younger brother, or by an uglier name, spiritual pride.

Perhaps with Miriam's starting it, they both criticized Moses for marrying a non-Jew. The woman Moses married was an Ethiopian or a Cushite. The name of Cush, the son of Ham, is applied in Scripture to both Africa and Arabia. Zipporah may have been called a Cushite, not as being herself of the children of Cush, but as belonging to a country which had received its name from them. This is the first time we see the contempt of Israel for other nations. Perhaps the return of Zipporah to the camp after having been with her father was the catalyst for this ugly display of jealousy.

Their Second Complaint

Since Miriam was a prophetess (Exodus 25:20) and Aaron was the High Priest, they wondered out loud why only Moses got to be the spokesman to the people from God. Scripture recorded this chilling statement: *"And the Lord heard it."* It is a serious matter to speak against a servant of God. The Lord will always guard jealously those who serve Him. Moses did not try to defend himself but humbly left that to God. Read this revealing verse: *"Now the man Moses was very humble, more than all men who were on the face of the earth."* What inward beauty Moses possessed!

The Lord will always guard jealously those who serve Him.

God Defends His Choice
Numbers 12:10-12

Miriam and Aaron were summoned to the tabernacle, and God Himself declared that Moses was His faithful servant. After God had finished speaking, the cloud departed, and Aaron saw that Miriam had been struck with leprosy. Aaron confessed their foolish and sinful behavior and asked Moses to pray for Miriam's healing. God's answer was immediate: *"If her father had but spit in her face, would she not be shamed seven days? Let her be shut out of the camp seven days, and afterward she may be received again."* A week-long lesson in humility was God's plan for Miriam. We would do well to learn from this episode and "humble ourselves" before God regularly.

The Turning Point Numbers 13:1-15:41	In the Chinese language, the **pictogram** for "crisis" is made of two symbols: opportunity and danger. Both apply here, since in these chapters Israel faces its biggest crisis yet, at the border of Canaan. Will they see it as their greatest opportunity or be paralyzed by its apparent danger?

> **pictogram** - character or symbol used in picture-writing

Spies Numbers 13:1-3	According to Deuteronomy 1:19-22, the Lord gave command to send spies into Canaan after the people requested it. They were not willing to go simply by faith in

the Word of God. He had told them that Canaan was a land flowing with milk and honey; therefore, they did not need to go there to confirm that fact. God had promised to give the land to them, so they did not need to go to evaluate the strength of the inhabitants. Their unbelief would cost them forty years and the death of an entire generation. Doubt and disobedience are very expensive.

A good lesson to learn here is that the majority is not always right when it comes to making spiritual decisions.

The Report of the Spies Numbers 13:25-14:4	The ten spies discouraged the people from obeying what God had told them to do by telling them that it would be impossible for them to overcome Canaan's powerful enemies. The whole camp of Israel was

influenced by the report of the majority. A good lesson to learn here is that the majority is not always right when it comes to making spiritual decisions.

Moses Prays for the Rebellious People Numbers 14:5-12	Caleb had tried to quiet the people before Moses. Moses himself tried to restore order and obedience (Deuteronomy 1:29) but without success. Moses and Aaron went before the Lord in earnest prayer, and the glory of the Lord appeared in the tabernacle in answer to their prayer. This was the second time God offered to start

the whole nation over with Moses as its only patriarch. It was a real offer to relieve him from the leadership of an unbelieving, rebellious people, but Moses would not abandon his people. He argued the case on their behalf before God, like an able defense attorney. He based his appeal for mercy on these facts:

1. Egypt will misunderstand. The unbelieving world, which has been witnessing Your supernatural protection of Israel, will hear You have killed them all and believe Your power was not strong enough to completely deliver them.
2. Your own Word proclaims Your Mercy. Moses quoted back to God the very words God had spoken to Moses when He revealed His glory to him. (See Exodus 34:6.) Moses reminded God that wiping out the whole nation was completely out of character to the Lord who is "abundant in mercy."

3. You have forgiven so many things in the past. Israel has been in and out of trouble since they left Egypt.

Moses succeeded; God spared the people but disciplined them in their rebellion. Only Joshua and Caleb would see the Promised Land; the children of Israel would turn to the wilderness and wander a year for each day that the spies had searched the land—until all the men twenty years old and upward had died in the desert. At Kadesh the people had rejected the land of promise and desired to return to Egypt. Deuteronomy 1:38 says they wept before the Lord but their tears were like those of Esau; the judgment of God could not be reversed. The children of Israel had despised their **birthright**.

> **birthright** - right, privilege, or possession to which a person is entitled

Death of the Ten Evil Spies
Numbers 14:36-37

The sudden death of the ten spies who brought back the evil report showed God's displeasure against those who sinned and tempted Israel to sin. Still not realizing the seriousness of their actions or the finality of God's Word, Israel thought they could reverse things by going on into the Promised Land on their own. But bravery without God's call was just as fatal as cowardice in response to God's call. They went out to battle in their own strength and were defeated.

God Keeps His Word
Numbers 15:1-41

"When you have come into the land you are to inhabit, which I am giving to you...." This was God's assurance that the children of Israel would certainly take possession of the land He promised them. After forty years of wandering in the wilderness, some would reach the land. God always keeps His promises, *"For the gifts and the calling of God are irrevocable"* (Romans 11:29), but our disobedience may delay them. The Lord told Moses that when they did finally possess the land, His laws and statutes would be in effect: *"That you may remember and do all My commandments, and be holy for your God"* (Numbers 15:40).

More Rebellion
Numbers 16 and 17

After the rebellion of Miriam and Aaron against Moses, the rebellion of Korah and some men from the tribe of Reuben occurred. Moses again was on his face, making no effort to defend himself, and left the dispute for the Lord to settle. Moses did recognize the selfish motives which inspired the men to rebel, but when the decision was given and the judgment of God was about to fall, he fell on his face before God pleading for the people he loved so much. God confirmed Moses' authority by judging the rebels with a supernaturally occurring death. Korah was one of the leaders of the family of Kohath. This tribe was assigned the work of carrying the ark and the furniture of the Holy of

Holies. They were of the tribe of Levi and probably felt it their right to contest the **exclusive** right of Aaron to the high priesthood. Dathan, Abiram and On were chiefs in the tribe of Reuben. It is probable that On withdrew from the conspiracy, as he is only mentioned once as being part of it. The Reubenites were discontent because the birthright had been taken away from their tribe due to the sin of Reuben, and they were no longer the leader of the tribes of Israel. So, they wanted the political power of Moses, while Korah and his group were after the spiritual position of Aaron. This conspiracy to overthrow Moses and to remove Aaron as High Priest was worse than any political plot, because it was rebellion against God who had appointed and empowered them. Those associated with the conspiracy were destroyed by God, and 14,700 people fell in this awful judgment. God confirmed the leadership of Aaron in Numbers 17 by the miracle of the rod that budded, bloomed, and produced almonds in one night.

> **exclusive** - limited to possession, control, or use by a single individual or group

> *This conspiracy to overthrow Moses and to remove Aaron as High Priest was worse than any political plot, because it was rebellion against God who had appointed and empowered them.*

> **tithes** - ten percent of one's wealth given to the support of a religious body

Responsibility and Privileges of the Priesthood
Numbers 18:1-19:22

This chapter made it clear that only Aaron and his sons were to be priests. The priests and the Levites who helped them were to be supported by the people with **tithes** and offerings.

The End of Three Leaders
Numbers 20:1-29

Skipping completely over Israel's "sentence" of forty years in the wilderness, this chapter recorded the events of the end of that period, when Israel returned to the place of their earlier rebellion, Kadesh. This is one of the saddest chapters in the book. It began with the death of Miriam, the one who had been the leader in the song of victory on the shores of the Red Sea after deliverance from Egypt. It ended with the death of Aaron, the one who had represented Israel in the Holy and Most Holy Place as High Priest. Between these two deaths we had the old story of murmuring on the part of the people and mercy on the part of God. We also had the sad situation of Moses himself disobeying the Word of God by striking the rock twice with the rod instead of speaking only to the rock as God had told him: a sin so serious that it excluded him as well as Aaron from entering the Promised Land.

Snake-bitten
Numbers 21:1-35

The Canaanite king of Arad, who dwelt in the south country, heard that Israel was coming through his land. He fought against Israel and took some of them as prisoners. This incident was recorded to reveal the hatred of Canaan for Israel. When Israel asked God for help, He responded and Israel utterly destroyed Canaan's cities. Yet, in spite of this victory, the people became discouraged and

Their looking on the serpent in the wilderness represented men believing in Christ and the power of Christ's death to save all those who believe on Him.

spoke against God and Moses, calling the manna "worthless bread." The punishment of the fiery serpents followed. When Israel repented, God provided a remedy in the serpent of brass, a model of the kind that bit them, raised on a pole. Christ explained the mystery of the brass serpent in His conversation with Nicodemus in John 12:32, *"And I, if I am lifted up from the earth, will draw all peoples to Myself."* Christ became a curse for us (Galatians 3:13) and was lifted up on a cross to bear the punishment we deserved. Their looking on the serpent in the wilderness represented men believing in Christ and the power of Christ's death to save all those who believe on Him. As there was no other cure for the snake-bitten victim but looking to the serpent on the pole, so there is no other cure for the sin-sick soul but to look to the sacrifice of Jesus on the cross.

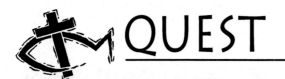

QUEST

Questions

Study Procedure: Read the Scripture references before answering questions. Unless otherwise instructed, use the Bible only in answering questions. Some questions may be more difficult than others but try to answer as many as you can. Pray for God's wisdom and understanding as you study and don't be discouraged if some answers are not obvious at first. Do not read the study notes for this lesson until AFTER you have completed your questions.

Note: It is difficult to cover this material in such a few short lessons, but please read your assigned chapters carefully, diligently work your questions, and read your notes. These chapters are full of many lesson applications.

MEMORY: LAMENTATIONS 3:25

Day One: Vocabulary Review

Fill in the blanks below with one of these words:

> rebuke   material   craving   pictograms   birthright   exclusive   tithes

1. "Stop it!" he shouted in an angry _____.

2. The elders brought in their _____ to the Levites.

3. Constantly eating manna, they soon developed a _____ for meat.

4. The land was theirs by _____.

5. They had forgotten their spiritual duties in pursuit of _____ things.

6. The tabernacle was for the _____ use of Israel's worship.

7. The symbols combined to picture a message are _____.

8. Read Numbers 21:10-20. Israel needed water again, but this time they did not murmur or complain. Find and record what happened to make this a pleasant experience.

   _____

   _____

   _____

   _____

9. Read Numbers 21:21-35. Name the kings and the countries that Israel defeated in this section. These victories will be mentioned many times throughout Israel's history.

   _____

   _____

   _____

   _____

10. Read Numbers 22, 23, and 24. Read also 2 Peter 2:15-16. The rights to the plains of Moab had been won by Israel when they conquered King Sihon earlier. Israel camped there and their large numbers alarmed Balak of Moab. For whom did Balak send and why?

_____

_____

Day Two:

MEMORY: JUDE 24-25

1. Read 2 Peter 2:15-16, Jude 11, and Revelation 2:14.
   a) Write down what is revealed about Balaam in these references. _____

_____

_____

_____

   b) From Numbers 22, 23, and 24 write down any phrases or actions that hint at the true character and sinfulness of Balaam._____

_____

_____

_____

_____

_____

2. Summarize the blessings or positive prophesies that were pronounced on Israel by Balaam.
   a) Numbers 23:7-10 _____

_____

   b) Numbers 23:18-24 _____

_____

_____

   c) Numbers 24:3-9_____

_____

   d) Numbers 24:15-19 _____

_____

3. Read Numbers 25 and Numbers 31:16. Even though Balaam did not curse Israel directly, he showed Balak how to tempt them. Into what sins did Israel fall? _____

_____

4. How many died as a result of their sin? _____

5. Describe the cause and result of Phinehas' actions. _____

_____

_____

_____

_____

_____

Day Three: Read Numbers 26

MEMORY: 1 PETER 3:12

1. a) Put a checkmark in the correct column as you
   compare the census figures from Numbers 1 with Numbers 26.

	Numbers 1	Numbers 26	Increase?	or	Decrease?
Reuben	46,500	43,730	_____		_____
Simeon	59,300	22,200	_____		_____
Gad	45,650	40,500	_____		_____
Judah	74,600	76,500	_____		_____
Issachar	54,400	64,300	_____		_____
Zebulun	57,400	60,500	_____		_____
Ephraim	40,500	32,500	_____		_____
Manasseh	32,200	52,700	_____		_____
Benjamin	35,400	45,600	_____		_____
Dan	62,700	64,400	_____		_____
Asher	41,500	53,400	_____		_____
Naphtali	53,400	45,400	_____		_____
Total	_____	_____	Difference	_____	

(Numbers 1:46)   (Numbers 26:51)

   b) The wilderness experience had affected them spiritually and physically. In Egypt they had
      multiplied, but not in the wilderness. Comment on the statement "faithfulness determines
      fruitfulness." _____

   _____

2. Read Numbers 27:1-11 and summarize the appeal of this early women's rights group. How was
   it settled? _____

   _____

   _____

   _____

   _____

3. Read Numbers 27:12-23.

a) What was Moses' concern when he was told it was time for him to die? _____

_____

b) How was his concern answered? _____

4. Read Numbers 28 and 29. List the holy days mentioned on which sacrifices were to be offered.

_____

_____

_____

5. From Chapter 30, write down at least one interesting regulation for making and keeping a vow.

_____

_____

_____

Day Four:

1. Read Numbers 31. The Midianites had joined Moab in hiring Balaam to help them against Israel
    and had tempted Israel to sin at Baal Peor, but now God was ready to judge Midian.

a) Find out why Moses was angry with Israel after the battle and record your findings below.

_____

_____

b) How were the captured animals divided among the people of Israel? _____

_____

_____

_____

c) How many men did Israel lose? _____

2. Read Numbers 32.

a) What tribes wanted to "stop short" of their final destination? _____

_____

b) What problems did Moses think this might cause? _____

_____

_____

c) How was it settled? _____

_____

_____

d) Can you relate this to Christian experience today? _____

_____

3. Read Numbers 33 and 34 and fill in the matching answers from the list below:

   a) Starting date of Israel's journeys _____

   b) Where Aaron died   _____

   c) How the land was to be divided among the tribes   _____

   d) Job description in Canaan   _____

   e) Southern border   _____

   f) Western border   _____

The Great Sea	drive out all the inhabitants
Wilderness of Zin to the Salt Sea	Mount Hor
first month, fifteenth day	by lot

MEMORY: MICAH 6:8

Day Five:

1. Read Numbers 35. Describe the location and purpose of the cities of refuge.

   _____

   _____

   _____

   _____

2. Read Numbers 36. What problem was brought before Moses to solve here, and what was his response?   _____

   _____

   _____

   _____

   _____

   _____

   _____

3. This has been a rapid overview of Numbers. Write down anything you would have liked to cover more completely.   _____

   _____

   _____

   _____

   _____

4. Now take a few minutes to read your study notes for this lesson.

Notes

Final Year in the Wilderness

Ready to Go In
Numbers 22-36

What is done outside the will of God is not noteworthy. Jesus put it bluntly: "Without Me you can do nothing."

Very little was recorded about those extra thirty-eight years the unbelieving generation of Israel spent in the wilderness. We read about some rebellion against the leadership of Moses and Aaron and the punishment that followed, but we did not find much recorded that was positive. There is a lesson for us even in the silence of the historical record. What is done outside the will of God is not noteworthy. Jesus put it bluntly: *"Without Me you can do nothing"* (John 15:5b). Thirty-eight wasted years. Near the end of the wanderings, with the older generation now dead and the younger one coming forward to lead, God allowed them to experience some military "tests" to prepare them for their battles in the Promised Land. They experienced dramatic victories over the Amorite kings, Sihon and Og. This last lesson in Numbers will focus on events which took place on the plains of the Jordan Valley to the north of Moab and the northeast of the Dead Sea during the final year in the wilderness.

Unholy Spiritual Warfare
Numbers 22:1-4

Human beings have an inborn sense about the supernatural. However, without the truth about God from Scriptures, they make up their own idea about divine power based on experience and superstition. A king of Moab named Balak had seen the huge group of Israelites camped over the land just taken from the the Amorite kings Sihon and Og. Balak, as was common, believed that a successful nation had to have the blessing and support of a powerful god. The God of Israel, he reasoned, must be superior if He enabled them to defeat such great enemies. Balak concluded that he and his gods could never defeat such a nation unless the God of Israel's blessing was removed. So, with the consent and help of the neighboring Midianites, he sent messengers to an area near the Euphrates River, the exact location being unknown, about a month's journey away, to a well-known prophet or seer named Balaam, whom he hoped to hire to curse Israel.

Balaam—Good or Bad?
Numbers 22:5-35

Few characters in Scripture are more interesting than Balaam. He was a Gentile, yet a prophet; he was experienced in the occult, yet enlightened with some knowledge of the true God. He was a man so well-known that a distant king sent for him to curse Israel, yet humble enough to seek God's will before traveling. Balaam's mixed interests or divided loyalties would be his downfall. It is probable that Balaam, like so many people in the countries near Egypt, knew something of what occurred when God miraculously delivered and protected Israel, as well as the giving of the law at Sinai, and the wilderness experiences. He regarded God as a mighty and perhaps even the Supreme Deity. On one occasion in Numbers 24:2 it says that the Spirit of God was present with him, but he was a tragic example of being gifted by God without being submissive to God. Scriptures recorded many others who were used by God in spite of their lack of complete faith in Him: Pharaoh, Abimelech, and Nebuchadnezzar are Gentile examples, while Samson and Saul come to mind from Israel.

| **New Testament Light on Balaam** | Before interpreting the Numbers record, it is helpful to see the "rest of the story" that the New Testament writers recorded about the character of Balaam. |

2 Peter 2:15-16: *"They have forsaken the right way and gone astray, following the way of Balaam the son of Beor, who loved the wages of unrighteousness; but he was rebuked for his iniquity: a dumb donkey speaking with a man's voice restrained the madness of the prophet."*

Jude 1:11: *"Woe to them! For they have gone in the way of Cain, have run greedily in the error of Balaam for profit, and perished in the rebellion of Korah."*

Revelation 2:14: *"But I have a few things against you, because you have there those who hold the doctrine of Balaam, who taught Balak to put a stumbling block before the children of Israel, to eat things sacrificed to idols, and to commit sexual immorality."*

In summary from these, then, Balaam, with his mixed motives, displeased God and hurt Israel. He proved true Jesus' teaching that no man can successfully serve two masters.

| **Back to the Numbers Record** | Balaam consulted God and refused King Balak's first invitation, but temptation to sin returned when the messengers came back with a better deal. Balaam did not |

resist this time, but, blinded with greed, he missed what even a donkey could see: God's displeasure. As shown by the talking donkey, God could use anything or anyone for His purposes, in spite of their motivation. Balaam was a mouthpiece for God, uttering four prophecies, blessing Israel even though he cooperated with King Balak in trying to find a way to do otherwise. In trying to please God and Balak, Balaam pleased neither. James in the New Testament wrote that *"he is a double-minded man, unstable in all his ways,"* and so *"let not that man suppose he will receive anything from the Lord"* (James 1:7-8). Balaam expressed what he saw as God's blessing on Israel in the first prophecy: *"Let me die the death of the righteous, and let my end be like his!"* (Numbers 23:10b). However, without being willing to live the life of a righteous man, Balaam was foolish to wish for such an end. He met an appropriate death for his double-life: killed by Israel's army as he lived among the Midianites, when God brought judgment on Israel's enemies for tempting them to idolatry (Numbers 31:8,16).

> *As shown by the talking donkey, God could use anything or anyone for His purposes, in spite of their motivation.*

Summarizing the Blessings

Numbers 23:9 (1) Israel would be preserved as a distinct nation. This is an amazing prophecy. No nation in the history of the world has been persecuted and scattered all over the planet, still able, as Israel has, to maintain their national identity enough to return finally in this century to their homeland. Mark Twain once wrote that if someone needed proof about the existence of God, he should look at Israel! God has not forgotten His people, and He will fulfill every promise to them yet. What an encouragement this must have been to the children of Israel at this time! Right in front of their enemies, God had Balaam declare their ultimate victory.

Numbers 23:21 (2) God promised to be present with them. This second prophecy might surprise us. Throughout this study we read of their constant rebellion, disobedience, and ingratitude, and God's chastisement of them for this. Yet, because *"God is not a man, that He should lie, nor a son of man, that He should repent,"* though many would die in unbelief, He would always preserve a remnant through which He would fulfill every promise He had ever given to Israel. No earthly or spiritual power would ever stop God from completing what He had started.

Numbers 24:7 (3) Israel will be a channel of blessing. The central ideas of this prophecy were prosperity and victory. God would continue to be, as He had been, the Source of all their blessings. He would use Israel as His channel of blessing for the rest of the nations.

Numbers 24:17 (4) Out of Israel will come a Redeemer. *"A Star shall come out of Jacob; a Scepter shall rise out of Israel."* These were symbols of royalty: the star stood for kingly glory, the scepter for royal power. This prophecy promised that a king would rise out of Israel. Not only their beloved King David is meant, but also, the greater son of David, Jesus Christ.

Balaam Returns "To His Place"
Numbers 24:25

From the New Testament references cited earlier, this evidently did not mean that Balaam went back to his own country. He remained among the Midianites to help them find another way to bring a curse on Israel. He could not go against the Spirit of God while he prophesied, but he was determined to please Balak and collect his wages another way: luring Israel into idolatry by appealing to their sexual lust. Satan still uses sex outside of marriage to tempt men and women away from their covenant with God and with each other. Woe to the one who sets the trap! That one will answer to God as surely as the one who takes the bait.

Satan still uses sex outside of marriage to tempt men and women away from their covenant with God and with each other.

Israel's Sickening Choice
Numbers 25

Midian and Moab invited Israel to join them for a feast following the sacrifices to their heathen gods. The main course, however, turned out to be sinful sexual activity. God judged His people with a plague that killed 24,000 of them. More deaths would have followed had one zealous priest named Phinehas not boldly executed a fellow Hebrew who **blatantly** brought a Midianite woman to Israel's camp. His willingness to act in righteous anger on God's behalf stopped further deaths by the plague.

blatantly - in a vulgar manner; offensively

Another Census
Numbers 26:1-65

This could be considered the third numbering of the children of Israel. The first numbering in Exodus 38:26, during the encampment at Sinai, was for the purpose of raising money for the tabernacle. In Numbers 1:2-3, a second census was taken as the Israelites began their journey from Sinai. This third census took place after the years of wilderness wanderings and before they entered the Promised Land. The population had decreased by 1,820. Remember back in Egypt that they had multiplied so phenomenally that

Pharaoh was frightened? Well, evidently their wilderness experience had not promoted population growth, even though it had probably been less physically rigorous than their oppressive Egyptian slavery. In spite of outward conditions, God was the source of blessing. When they responded to His commands in unbelief and disobedience, He did not release the blessing of growth. The "wilderness" Christian, unsurrendered and murmuring, should likewise not expect God's blessing on his or her life.

> *When they responded to His commands in unbelief and disobedience, He did not release the blessing of growth. The "wilderness" Christian, unsurrendered and murmuring, should likewise not expect God's blessing on his or her life.*

Early Women's Rights: The Daughters of Zelophehad
Numbers 27:1-11

Land was inherited from father to son. Zelophehad had died, not because of any of the rebellions, but "in his own sin," and left only daughters. As the law stood then, they would not be eligible to receive land when they arrived in Canaan. They had faith to believe that God would bring Israel to Canaan and wanted to make sure that they would share in the land. Moses consulted God and issued a change in the civil code, allowing women to inherit in the absence of male heirs. This was a revolutionary idea at that early date, showing God's eternal justice and mercy for all people, male or female. Later, in Numbers 36, there would be an amendment to this law, restricting the heiresses to marriage within their own tribe to insure that the land would remain within the holdings of the tribe of Manasseh, as would have been the case with male heirs.

Announcement of the Death of Moses and the Choice of Joshua
Numbers 27:12-23

Although Moses was a faithful servant of the Lord, he once rebelled against God's commandment and failed in his duty as a leader. The Scripture warned about the result of sin in leadership: *"My brethren, let not many of you become teachers, knowing that we shall receive a stricter judgment" (James 3:1)*. Those who hold places of honor and responsibility in the work of God must be constantly aware of the effect of their words and actions on others. The time of death for Moses was approaching, and God reminded him of this, as well as of his sin of rebellion before the people. Moses received the message humbly, only expressing concern over who would take his place so *"that the congregation of the Lord may not be like sheep which have no shepherd."* God answered Moses by telling him to lay his hands on Joshua before the congregation of Israel and the high priest Eleazar and **inaugurate** him there. We do not have to say good-bye to Moses here, though. The entire book of Deuteronomy records the last days and last words of the great law-giver.

inaugurate - to induct into an office with suitable ceremonies

The Offerings and Special Days
Numbers 28:1-29:40

God rehearsed the importance of the offerings and the feasts in Chapters 28 and 29. The repetition of the phrase *"to the Lord"* emphasized their real purpose. Perhaps the thirty-eight extra years in the wilderness had made Israel mechanical or careless in their worship. Before they entered Canaan, they must be reminded that these services should never be seen as repetitious rituals. Perhaps we need to evaluate our attitude toward worship. What is our focus? Is all we do as a part of our organized worship done *"to the Lord"*?

> *Perhaps the thirty-eight extra years in the wilderness had made Israel mechanical or careless in their worship.*

Laws Concerning Vows
Numbers 30:1-16

This chapter recorded the regulations about vow-making. In an earlier lesson we discussed that, though not required, vows were acceptable to God as a way for a person to express extra devotion or perform more-than-required service in thanksgiving to God. Recognizing the order God established for the home, the laws allowed for a husband or a father to over-rule any inappropriate vows made by those under his authority, but required every grown man to keep any vow he had made.

Judgment upon the Midianites
Numbers 31:1-54

The Midianites and Moabites had been **hostile** toward Israel without Israel's having done anything to cause such behavior. God allowed Israel now to be his instrument for judgment on Midian. Perhaps the Moabites were spared for the time being because they had been led into opposing Israel by Midian. It was at this time that Balaam, who was found still living among them, was killed, too. All the men of Midian were slain, their cities burned, and their valuables taken. Moses had to reprimand his army for sparing the women and male children. The women had been a part of the temptation into sexual sin and idolatry; while the male children were bound to grow up to avenge their nation. The judgment had to be total and **impartial**. It was a **graphic** example of God's sure judgment on sin and certain justice on behalf of His people. Israel would face many more battles. In this one they did not lose a single man.

> **hostile** - unfriendly; of or relating to an enemy

> **impartial** - fair; unbiased

> **graphic** - marked by clear and lively description

Land East of Jordan Divided
Numbers 32:1-42

With Midian destroyed, the Israelites took possession of the area east of Jordan. This was beautiful pasture land, and the children of Gad and the children of Reuben requested it for themselves. These two tribes *"had a very great multitude of livestock,"* and the territory would give them fertile land. They were anxious to possess it. The half-tribe of Manasseh evidently made the same request. (See verse 33.)

Moses was very concerned about the results of such a change in the plans from going over the Jordan to Canaan. Would it not bring on the judgment of God for two tribes to fail to support the others? Hadn't they all been in enough trouble for rebellion and lack of faith already? However, after hearing them pledge their complete support to the efforts of their brothers on the other side of the river, Moses gave consent to the request of the Reubenites and the Gadites after requiring them to meet certain conditions.

Moses said, in essence, that if they were disobedient to the terms, they would realize it when their sin overtook them. The sad parallel here to so many of our lives is that we want to stop short of what God has called us to do and settle for the nearer, quicker benefit instead of pushing on in with others to the place or task that God has planned for us to fulfill. When we stop short, we put a greater burden on our brothers and sisters, who feel compelled to obey completely.

> *The sad parallel here to so many of our lives is that we want to stop short of what God has called us to do and settle for the nearer, quicker benefit instead of pushing on in with others to the place or task that God has planned for us to fulfill.*

Summary of Israel's Journey
Numbers 33:1-56

God had written into the record all the stops of their forty-year escape from Egypt. Now the time had come to enter Canaan and **expel** the inhabitants, who had been polluting the land for four hundred years with their idolatrous practices.

expel - to force out

Boundaries Recorded
Numbers 34:1-29

The boundary lines were described in detail. The River Jordan formed the eastern border, and an irregular curve extending over the desert from the southern extreme of the Dead Sea to the River of Egypt formed the southern border. In all the other passages where the boundaries are mentioned (Genesis 15; Exodus 23; Deuteronomy 1:11; 2 Samuel 18; 1 Kings 4; 2 Chronicles 8:9), the Euphrates is mentioned as the eastern limit. In Exodus 23:31 the boundary of Israel is described as stretching to the south as far as the Red Sea. There is no contradiction here. The boundary of the Holy Land which the Israelites were to divide after the Canaanites were driven out was one thing; the boundary beyond which they were not to go in future conquests was another. God promised the larger area to them as their ultimate possession.

Levitical Cities
Numbers 35:1-34

Levi was not to inherit a single large portion of land like the other tribes, but, instead, it was to receive forty-eight cities in different parts of the land. These would be strategically located so as to serve as headquarters for the Levites as they performed their religious duties of instructing the people. Six cities out of the forty-eight allotted to the Levites were given or established as cities of refuge. They were to be cities in which someone guilty of manslaughter, not murder, might find protection from a member of the slain person's family wanting vengeance. Murder was always punishable by death, but manslaughter or accidental death required a hearing. Meanwhile, the one responsible could find safety in one of the six cities until judgment could be decided.

Last Chapter of Numbers
Numbers 36:1-13

This book concludes with *"these are the commandments and the judgments which the Lord commanded the children of Israel by the hand of Moses in the plains of Moab by the Jordan, across from Jericho."* They were about to enter Canaan and God wanted them completely informed about what He required. It is a good thing to remember that when God directs, He also educates. He will provide what is needed to do what He requires. Our job like Israel's is to trust Him, hear His instructions, and obey.

It is a good thing to remember that when God directs, He also educates. He will provide what is needed to do what He requires.

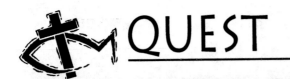

QUEST

LESSON 19

Questions

Study Procedure: Read the Scripture references before answering questions. Unless otherwise instructed, use the Bible only in answering questions. Some questions may be more difficult than others but try to answer as many as you can. Pray for God's wisdom and understanding as you study and don't be discouraged if some answers are not obvious at first. Do not read the study notes for this lesson until AFTER you have completed your questions.

Day One: Review of the book of Numbers: Match the following

____1. Joshua	a)	had a talking donkey
____2. Levites	b)	two Amorite kings defeated by Israel
____3. Judah	c)	population count
____4. census	d)	keepers of the tabernacle
____5. Kibroth Hattaavah	e)	Caleb's tribe
____6. Ephraim	f)	next leader of Israel
____7. Balaam	g)	Miriam's punishment
____8. tassels	h)	number of tribes staying east of the Jordan
____9. Zelophehad	i)	led a rebellion
____10. Sihon and Og	j)	striking the rock at Kadesh
____11. Korah	k)	graves of craving
____12. 2 1/2	l)	placed on corners of men's robes to remind them to obey God's commands
____13. Moses' sin	m)	Joshua's tribe
____14. 7-day leprosy	n)	father who died without male heirs, and girls asked for right of inheritance

Day Two: Read Deuteronomy 1

MEMORY: DEUTERONOMY 1:21

We will have five lessons on Deuteronomy, each focusing on one of the three sermons Moses delivered to Israel's new generation of leaders. It has been called the book of the second chance, since the nation stood again on the threshold of the Promised Land.

1. a) How long did it normally take to travel from Mount Horeb (Sinai) to Kadesh, the entry point to Canaan? _____

   b) How long had it taken Israel this last time? _____

2. What is the date of this opening speech by Moses to Israel? _____

_____

3. Read Deuteronomy 1:3 and 34:8 and Joshua 4:19 and calculate how long it took Moses to give the three sermons of Deuteronomy. _____

4. There are several details supplied in this chapter about Israel's failure 38 years before when they were at Kadesh Barnea. Record below any new information you discover about the following:

    a) division of leadership (verse 15) _____

    _____

    b) the request for spies (verse 22) _____

    _____

    c) complaint in the tents (verse 27) _____

    _____

    d) Israel's real problem (verse 32) _____

    e) when God revealed His choice of Moses' replacement (verses 37-38) _____

    _____

    f) why those under 20 were spared from judgment (verse 39) _____

    _____

Day Three: Read Deuteronomy 2

MEMORY: JOHN 8:47

1. a) Esau and Lot were relatives of Israel (Jacob) as recorded back in Genesis. What promises to their descendants was God still keeping?

    _____

    b) How does that make you feel about promises available to you in Scripture? _____

    _____

    _____

2. What verse summarizes God's care of Israel during the previous 40 years? _____

3. Record any information you find here about giants. Consult a Bible dictionary for more help.

    _____

    _____

    _____

    _____

4. Read verse 25. Comment on God's use of "publicity" to help His people. _____

    _____

    _____

5. Verse 31 has an important principle for success in Christian work: Begin to _____ it, that you may _____ the land. Rewrite this in your own words. _____

_____

_____

Day Four: Read Deuteronomy 3

MEMORY: **2 TIMOTHY 1:7**

1. Moses reminds them of two of their most recent victories. Name them. _____

_____

2. What was most interesting about the defeat of King Og? _____

3. What was God's purpose in giving them these early war experiences? _____

_____

_____

4. List some past victories that you have experienced that should **make you** hopeful about current battles facing you. _____

_____

_____

5. a) What personal incident in verses 23-29 does Moses reveal? _____

_____

_____

b) Share your thoughts or feelings about this. _____

_____

_____

_____

c) Read Matthew 17:1-5 and write down what you find about the time Moses did get to enter the Promised Land. _____

_____

_____

Day Five: Read Deuteronomy 4

MEMORY: **JOHN 1:1-5**

This is a wonderful chapter on the importance of knowing God and His Word. From Deuteronomy 4:1-10, fill in the blanks with the verse numbers that express these truths:

1. The Word of God is complete as written. _____

2. The commandments of God are the source of wisdom and understanding. _____

3. It will take effort to learn and remember them. _____

4. Children must be taught them, too. _____

5. Fill in the blanks with the important descriptions of God's nature:

   a) God is _____ (verse 24).

   b) God is _____ (verse 31).

   c) The Lord Himself is _____

   _____ (verse 39).

6. What verses gave help and hope to Israel whenever they sinned? _____

7. Now take a few minutes to read your study notes for this lesson.

Notes

Israel at the Edge of Canaan

The Book of Deuteronomy Deuteronomy came from a word which literally meant the "Second Law." It is not a set of new laws, but it is a serious review by Moses of the requirements and history of Israel's covenant relationship with God. Moses delivered the three sermons that make up Deuteronomy during the last forty days of his life. He was making sure that the younger generation of Israelites, who had survived to take over the leadership from their unbelieving parents, was fully informed of the truths about their God: His promises to them and His requirements of them.

The Wonderful Word of God In Deuteronomy 1, Moses emphasized the need for individuals to hear, study, and obey God's Word and warned that careful teaching of Scripture to children must continue for the nation to remain strong. Unfortunately, Moses' advice was not followed consistently. Hundreds of years later, there was an episode recorded in 2 Kings 22 and 2 Chronicles 34 which told of a time when the book of Deuteronomy was not taught to anyone—because they did not know it existed! However, after the wicked reign of Manasseh and Amon, King Josiah commanded that the house of the Lord be repaired and cleansed of all the false worship brought in by King Manasseh. In the process of cleaning out the temple, the workers found the book of Deuteronomy. Here it had been stored, unnoticed and unread for many years. King Josiah had it read before the people. The king and people alike were horrified when they heard God's judgment against idolatry. Josiah began to make even more corrections in

The king and people alike were horrified when they heard God's judgment against idolatry.

obedience to Deuteronomy's clear message. Casual neglect of God's Word leads to forgetfulness and then ignorance of it. Yet, any attempt to obey, as Josiah did, what is known about God's will, will open the way for God to "uncover" more and more from His Word about Himself.

To neglect God's Word today is just as serious a matter as it was in the history of Israel. Scriptural ignorance led them to heathenism and idolatry. Such ignorance leads nations today into immorality, violence, materialism, and devaluing of human life. Christians should listen to the solemn warnings of Deuteronomy about neglecting the study of the Word of God. Many churches operate today, busily unaware that Scripture has been "lost" from their seminaries or local planning boards. Its rediscovery still causes great movements of repentance and reform, and that is why Bible studies such as Explorer's have a vital role to play in bringing groups and individuals back in contact with God's Word.

Many churches operate today, busily unaware that Scripture has been "lost" from their seminaries or local planning boards.

These are the three sermons or divisions of Deuteronomy that we will use in our study:

Chapters 1-4	Moses summarized God's past faithfulness to Israel and the importance of hearing and obeying God's Word.
Chapters 5-26	Beginning with the Ten Commandments, Moses restates and applies God's laws. Jesus quoted from Deuteronomy in His teachings more than from any other book, so students can expect to read many familiar-sounding passages.
Chapter 27-34	Moses presented the warnings for disobedience and reviewed the blessings for obedience to God. This section ends with the account of Moses' death.

Opening Explanation
Deuteronomy 1:1-5

"These are the words which Moses spoke to all Israel on this side of the Jordan in the wilderness." Moses delivered a final series of sermons at the age of 120, during the final forty days of his life. He started the sermons on the first day of the eleventh month of the fortieth year. That left a total of sixty days, or two months, remaining in that year. Joshua led the people into the Promised Land on the tenth day of the first month of the next year, according to Joshua 4:19. That made a total of seventy days in that period. According to Deuteronomy 34:8, the people mourned thirty days over the death of Moses that occurred in that time-frame. So, that left forty days for Moses to have given and recorded the three sermons recorded in Deuteronomy.

Reviewing the Past
Deuteronomy 1:6-8

Moses first took his listeners back to the days of their childhood, when after witnessing the power of God at Mount Sinai in the region of Horeb and hearing the Ten Commandments and plans for the tabernacle issued, they were told the words of God: *"You have dwelt long enough at this mountain. Turn and take your journey...to the land of the Canaanites."* Everything had been done on the part of God and Moses to bring Israel immediately to the land promised to them since the days of Abraham. All they needed to do was to go forward in faith and possess what God had promised. However, through unbelief, they failed miserably.

All they needed to do was to go forward in faith and possess what God had promised. However, through unbelief, they failed miserably.

Leaders Appointed
Deuteronomy 1:9-18

For the benefit of the new generation of leaders coming out of the wilderness, Moses repeated the reason leaders were chosen, their qualifications, and their varying levels of responsibility. The emphasis was on fairness to all over whom they held authority. No **partiality** was to be shown, even in the cases of strangers against Israelites or rich against poor. This command would often be repeated in the New Testament writings, too.

partiality - related to the part rather than the whole; favoritism

Failure without Faith
Deuteronomy 1:19-33

Moses continued the history lesson with the tragic story of the spies who discouraged the people with their report about Canaan and its inhabitants. The bottom-line was powerfully pointed out by Moses for their learning: *"Yet, for all that, you did not believe the Lord your God, who went in the way before you to search out a place for you to pitch your tents, to show you the way you should go, in the fire by night and in the cloud by day."* Unbelief brought failure.

Dying Off in the Wilderness
Deuteronomy 1:34-45

The generation listening to Moses here had been under twenty-years-old, with *"no knowledge of good and evil,"* at the time of their parents' unbelieving response to the challenge to enter Canaan. Over the next thirty-eight years, those older than twenty had died, and the younger generation grew up to start again. Moses **frankly** pointed out to his listeners his own disqualification from entering the Promised Land because of his sin at Rephidim.

frankly - sincerely expressed

God's Care and Warning
Deuteronomy 2

God had directed their travels in the wilderness, too. He had not abandoned His people even while **chastening** them. God warned them to leave the people of Esau, Moab, and Ammon alone in their settlements, since He had given them their lands long ago. All three were only distantly related to this present Israel,

chastening - pruning of excess; correcting through punishment

and not very godly, but God kept His word to them through the years. Certainly, then, He would keep every promise to His own covenant people.

God had never forsaken Israel: *"For the Lord your God has blessed you in all the work of your hand. He knows your trudging through this great wilderness. These forty years, the Lord your God has been with you; you have lacked nothing"* (Deuteronomy 2:7).

> **Emim** - "terrible ones"; giants

Giants Galore!
Deuteronomy 2 and 3

The old generation had feared entering Canaan the first time because of the report of giants. But God allowed the younger generation to be exposed to giants in the wilderness—the **Emim**, Avim, and Anakim were mentioned. Israel even had success in defeating a giant Amorite king named Og, whose bed was described as 13 1/2 feet long by 6 feet wide. The two victories over Sihon and Og were to encourage this new Israeli leadership in going forward bravely to face the enemies of Canaan. *"You must not fear them,"* Moses explained, *"for the Lord your God Himself fights for you"* (Deuteronomy 3:22).

2 1/2 Tribes Ready to Stop
Deuteronomy 3:12-20

After the conquest of the two Amorite kings, the conquered territory east of Jordan was divided among the tribes of Reuben, Gad, and Manasseh at their request. The tribe of Manasseh received one-half of its inheritance on the east side of the Jordan and the other half on the west. Even though these tribes settled here, they were to cross over Jordan and help in the conquest of the Promised Land. Their wives and children would stay in the shelter of the cities east of Jordan while the men went to war.

> *Moses did not cross Jordan, as David did not see the temple, nor Daniel the return, nor John the Baptist the revelation of Christ's glory. Yet to all these servants God gave a prophetic vision that was sure to come to pass.*

Stop Right There!
Deuteronomy 3:23-29

Moses did not hide his own problems from the people. He told them of trying to appeal to God for another chance to go forward with the nation he loved. But God had already settled that and responded firmly, *"Enough of that! Speak no more to Me of this matter."* God urged Moses to go up to a high point and look the land over but reminded him that Joshua was the one chosen to take them in. Moses did not cross Jordan, as David did not see the temple, nor Daniel the return, nor John the Baptist the revelation of Christ's glory. Yet to all these servants God gave a prophetic vision that was sure to come to pass.

Conclusion of First Message
Deuteronomy 4

Moses ended his first message with an emphasis and an appeal. The emphasis was on the unique power and value of the Word of God, and the appeal was for obedience to it.

The statutes and judgments of God were so wonderful, that if Israel obeyed them, she would certainly possess all that God had planned for her in the new land. Israel was not to try to improve God's Word with additions or corrections, remembering how God punished the idolatrous activities at Baal Peor. Moses' audience, he pointed out, was alive today only because of their obedience to God's Word (verse 4). The laws God entrusted to Israel would be the laws that set the foundation for godly governments centuries later, including our own. They must be preserved and passed down to every new generation very carefully. The repeated warnings about the importance of teaching these laws emphasized the natural tendency of a nation to minimize or neglect moral education of its young, as we have seen, with tragic results, in our own country.

"Take Heed to Yourselves"
Deuteronomy 4:15-30

Three times Moses warned them in this section to "take heed," or beware of being drawn away from the true God to idols. He reminded them that God had never revealed Himself to them in any kind of form that could be copied, manufactured, and then falsely worshiped. Even the majesty of the heavenly bodies was not to be idolized, for God created them and gave them to the world. God is *"a consuming fire, a jealous God,"* and will not tolerate false worship. The way to worship the true God is to *"seek Him with all your heart and with all your soul...turn to the Lord your God and obey His voice."*

heed - to pay attention

He reminded them that God had never revealed Himself to them in any kind of form that could be copied, manufactured, and then falsely worshiped.

Israel: One of a Kind
Deuteronomy 4:32-40

"For ask now concerning the days that are past, which were before you, since the day that God created man on the earth, and ask from one end of heaven to the other...," Moses challenged Israel, because she could never find another nation to which God had revealed Himself so clearly and protected so publicly. Christians could ask the same question. Has there ever been a group that was allowed to know and love God as the people whom He has redeemed by the blood of His Only Son? Now as then, God is entitled to wholehearted obedience. This fourth chapter of Deuteronomy closed with a serious appeal that has value today: *"Keep His statutes and His commandments which I command you today, that it may go well with you and with your children after you."*

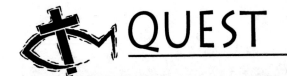

Questions

Study Procedure: Read the Scripture references before answering questions. Unless otherwise instructed, use the Bible only in answering questions. Some questions may be more difficult than others but try to answer as many as you can. Pray for God's wisdom and understanding as you study and don't be discouraged if some answers are not obvious at first. Do not read the study notes for this lesson until AFTER you have completed your questions.

Day One: Vocabulary Review: Choose the best synonym for each of these vocabulary words found in your notes.

_____1. frankly   a) quickly   b) quietly   c) honestly

_____2. partiality   a) in little pieces   b) favoritism   c) impatience

_____3. chastening   a) disciplining   b) baptizing   c) polishing

_____4. heed   a) see and forget   b) hear and obey   c) hide and seek

_____5. Emim   a) giants   b) sailors   c) insects

6. Why was it important for Moses to review the history of Israel and laws of God at this particular time?
    a) He needed the practice.
    b) The adults in the audience were just children the last time he taught it.
    c) They were about to enter the Promised Land and would need to know exactly what God required since they would need His blessing as they started living on their individual properties.
    d) None of the above.

7. From your notes or from your own experience, what is the responsibility of each generation to the next in regard to knowledge of the Bible? _____

_____

_____

Day Two: Read Deuteronomy 5. (You have had questions about the Ten Commandments in an earlier lesson in Exodus, but this is the week that they will be presented in more detail.)
    1. From verse 1, what was Moses' purpose in calling the nation together to hear God's law?
        "That you may _____ _____ and be _____ to
        _____ _____."

2. Select three commandments and rephrase them in your own words. Then add a sentence or two of explanation about each that would help a new Bible student or even an unbeliever understand their meaning.

Commandment _____ _____

_____

_____

_____

_____

_____

Commandment _____ _____

_____

_____

_____

_____

_____

Commandment _____ _____

_____

_____

_____

_____

_____

Day Three: Read Deuteronomy 6 and 7

MEMORY: DEUTERONOMY 5:7-10

1. From 6:1-3, what are the benefits of hearing and obeying the Word of God? _____

_____

_____

2. Read Matthew 22:37. Which verse in Deuteronomy 6 was Jesus quoting? _____

3. What things did Moses warn them about that might make them forget God? (See Deuteronomy 6:10-12.) _____

_____

_____

4. From Deuteronomy 7, why did God choose Israel? _____

_____

_____

5. In what specific ways does God bless obedience? (Deuteronomy 7:12-26) _____

_____

_____

_____

_____

Day Four: Read Deuteronomy   **MEMORY: DEUTERONOMY 5:11-12,16-21**
8 and 9

1. In what situation did Jesus quote Deuteronomy 8:3? (See Luke 4:1-13.) _____

_____

2. Don't miss Deuteronomy 8:4: *"Your garments did not wear out on you, nor did your foot swell these forty years".* What do you think of that? _____

_____

_____

3. What does Moses make clear to Israel in Deuteronomy 9:3-13 to keep them from having a wrong attitude of pride? Circle the appropriate answers.

   a) You were not picked by God because of your good record.

   b) The heathen will be driven out from the land because of their years of sin and rebellion against God.

   c) God's blessings on you are because He is keeping the promises He made to Abraham, Isaac, and Jacob.

   d) You really blew it the time I went to that forty-day conference at Horeb!

4. What does Moses mean when he calls them "stiff-necked"? (Deuteronomy 9:6,13)

   a) crippled

   b) stubborn and rebellious

   c) ignorant

MEMORY: DEUTERONOMY 6:4

Day Five: Read Deuteronomy 10

1. What does God require of Israel here that He still desires from us now? (See Deuteronomy 10:12-13.) _____

_____

_____

_____

_____

2. Explain in your own words Deuteronomy 10:16: *"Therefore circumcise the foreskin of your heart, and be stiff-necked no longer."* _____

_____

_____

_____

3. From Deuteronomy 10:19, why were they to show mercy to strangers? _____

_____

4. Make a note of any verse in this lesson about which you would like to know more.

_____

5. Now, go "digging" and explore that verse. Make a note of what you found and where and how you found it in the space below. _____

_____

_____

_____

_____

6. Now take a few minutes to read your study notes for this lesson.

Notes

The Ten Commandments

Ready to Go In   After the first message or sermon (Deuteronomy 1-4) Moses probably dismissed his audience so that they could think about what he had said. Reassembling them later, Moses gave them the next message, his longest, and recorded the text beginning with Deuteronomy 4:44: *"Now this is the law which Moses set before the children of Israel."* The sermon continued through Chapter 30. It is packed full of powerful passages; many sounded familiar because they were quoted or alluded to frequently in the New Testament. Jesus Himself often quoted Deuteronomy, the most memorable time being when He was tempted by Satan in the wilderness (see Matthew or Luke 4) and responded with Deuteronomy 8:3, 6:16, and 6:13.

The emphasis for lecture and notes for this lesson was the Ten Commandments. You read them in the earlier lessons on Exodus, but the study of them was saved till now.

The Ten Commandments
Deuteronomy 5:1-21

The purpose for Moses' teaching blitz on the commandments of God during the last few weeks of his life was summarized in Deuteronomy 5:1: *"that you may learn them and be careful to observe them."* These words make up the theme of the entire book of Deuteronomy, which emphasizes moral responsibility and practical obedience. Moses had reminded them of making covenant with God at Horeb. How could they ever forget that day? He emphasized that though they were children on that occasion, the covenant still included them: *"The Lord did not make this covenant with our fathers, but with us, those who are here today, all of us who are alive"* (Deuteronomy 5:3). Remember that this covenant formed the basis of their relationship to God. In covenant there was a joining of identities and a sharing of resources. Sealed with blood, the symbol of life, a covenant was binding till one of the partners died. They had not earned a place in covenant with the Creator of the universe, but they had accepted it when it was offered to them and had continually enjoyed the benefits that had come from it. The laws or commands of God that Moses emphasized were the terms of the covenant that they had agreed to keep. It was a serious matter to violate the terms or promises of a covenant, and Moses wanted them to remember that with the benefits they enjoyed, there came responsibilities.

It was a serious matter to violate the terms or promises of a covenant, and Moses wanted them to remember that with the benefits they enjoyed, there came responsibilities.

The First Commandment
Deuteronomy 5:7

"You shall have no other gods before Me." This first commandment clearly stated that God would not tolerate worship of anyone or anything except Himself. He had revealed Himself in Scripture and in action as the only true God, Maker of Heaven and Earth, and there was no other god in charge. He is the Truth, and worship of any other would be a lie. The foundation of our faith rests on this truth, expressed in the Jewish "Shema" or "hear" of Deuteronomy 6:4: *"Hear, O Israel: The Lord our God, the Lord is one."* A verse later this continued, *"You shall love the Lord your God with all your heart, with all your soul, and with all your strength."*

This commandment was given first, because without it, the rest could not be obeyed. Moses knew that the biggest threat to real faith was not an absolute denial of God—only a fool says in his heart there is no God (Psalm 14:1)—but instead, the biggest threat was to give any worship to anything or anyone besides God. Aaron, in the episode of the golden calf, added a deity to Israel's worship. Whenever someone worships God "plus," there is danger. The first commandment demands that we search our hearts to see if there is anything at all that rivals our love for God. Whatever or whoever it is must be identified and put down. In the words of a hymn, "I dare not trust the sweetest frame, but wholly lean on Jesus' Name. On Christ the solid Rock I stand; all other ground is sinking sand."

The Second Commandment
Deuteronomy 5:8

"You shall not make for yourself a carved image." This prohibits the practice of idolatry. God never gave a "viewing" of Himself that could be copied and made into an idol. So, all representations of God by anything man-made or naturally occurring are false and limit the concept of God in the worshiper. God hates this practice. He is Spirit and would have us think of Him in glorious power, wisdom, righteousness, holiness and love. Our thoughts are limited, but what we know of God from His Word is true.

The last part of verse 9 of Deuteronomy 5 was a warning describing the results of obedience or disobedience to the second commandment: *"visiting the iniquity of the fathers upon the children to the third and fourth generations of those who hate Me, but showing mercy to thousands, to those who love Me and keep My commandments."* This statement did not mean that God punishes the innocent children of ungodly parents or the converted children of unbelieving parents for the sins of the parents. The judgment falls only upon the children who walked in their fathers' footsteps and "hated the Lord." God deals with every man personally and directly according to his individual relationship to Him. (Read Ezekiel 18:19-20.) However, from observations made in the lives around us, we can see that faithful parents "pave the way" for their children to come to faith, while unfaithful parents hinder the spiritual development of their children. So while each person is individually accountable to God, what he or she does can greatly affect the lives of those watching. There are long-term consequences for sin and long-term benefits for obedience. These both affect the generations that come after us.

Faithful parents "pave the way" for their children to come to faith, while unfaithful parents hinder the spiritual development of their children. So while each person is individually accountable to God, what he or she does can greatly affect the lives of those watching.

The Third Commandment
Deuteronomy 5:11

"You shall not take the name of the Lord your God in vain." We could not know God if He had not chosen to reveal Himself by names, descriptive titles, or expressed characteristics. It is common to hear a name of a person and immediately make a mental association with a place or a cause or a specific activity. God is so unique and special that we should not speak His name in any way that allows a listener to associate it with anything except perfect godliness. A warning was given to any who might be careless in this: *"The Lord will not hold him guiltless."*

The Fourth Commandment
Deuteronomy 5:12-15

"Observe the Sabbath day, to keep it holy." The Exodus reading was, *"Remember the Sabbath day, to keep it holy. Six days you shall labor and do all your work."* This

law related to labor and rest. God intended that man work diligently and faithfully, earning an honest living six days a week, but it is in the interest of man's physical and spiritual well-being that God commanded he observe a day for rest and worship. *"The seventh day is the Sabbath of the Lord your God."* The sabbath day was to be kept by being sanctified or set apart for worship and rest. It was meant to be a blessing for man.

From Seventh to the First Day

The resurrection of Jesus Christ occurred on the first day of the week. It was such a special day that Christians adopted it as their day of meeting in the early Church. Several references to this change are found in the book of Acts. The principle of this commandment when applied to the Christian's body is that one day out of seven should be given to resting from the ordinary daily labor so that a person can be refreshed physically; spiritually applied, the principle insures that one day focused on holy activities would renew the inner man. Although the modern world seems to ignore it, the Lord's Day provides Christians with opportunities for joyful fellowship, worship, and needed rest.

Four and Six

The first four commandments have to do with maintaining right fellowship with God. The last six have to do with our interaction with our fellow human beings. Of course, top on the list would be our first human relationship, that of child to parents.

The Fifth Commandment Deuteronomy 5:16

"Honor your father and your mother, as the Lord your God has commanded you, that your days may be long, and that it may be well with you in the land which the Lord your God is giving you." Honor includes love, reverence and obedience. Throughout Scripture, God gives honor to the institution of the family. The relationship to an earthly father was to picture and pave the way for the one we have with our Heavenly Father. As a child is growing up, the parent stands as the supreme authority figure to him. Before the child knows who God is, or whether there is a God, the parent is teaching him about what a relationship with an authority is all about. As the child learns to honor father and mother, he is being prepared to honor God as his Heavenly Father and give to Him the obedience he has learned to give earthly parents. Whenever the commandment to honor parents has been neglected or corrupted, the family structure, as well as the larger community of which it is a part, begins to disintegrate. Families are the strength of society, but without a respect for authority, children will neither honor their parents, keeping the family intact, nor look to the authority of God for direction of their lives. We only have to look around to see the results of this broken commandment.

The relationship to an earthly father was to picture and pave the way for the one we have with our Heavenly Father.

The fifth commandment was the only commandment with a blessing promised for keeping it. The apostle Paul quoted it in Ephesians 6:2-3, indicating that this promise still applies to Christians in the New Testament.

The Sixth Commandment
Deuteronomy 5:17

"You shall not murder." The Hebrew word for murder here means the intentional killing of another to accomplish an evil purpose. The true reason for this prohibition is expressed in Genesis 9:6: *"Whoever sheds man's blood, by man his blood shall be shed; for in the image of God He made man."* The death penalty was authorized and demanded, not from cruelty, but on the ground of the sacredness of human life. This sixth commandment actually protected life. Since every person is created in the image of God, his life is as precious as any other and deserves protection. This command did not forbid killing in necessary defense, as in a war, and neither did it forbid putting offenders to death. If an individual willfully and maliciously murdered another, he forfeited his right to life. Someone wrote, "The estimate placed by a lawgiver upon any right can be measured only by the penalty by which he guards it." Death is the ultimate penalty; imposing it showed the highest possible estimate of the value of life. Many reject the death penalty, persuading themselves and others that they value life too much to require that. However, in reality, they are saying that life is not valuable enough to be protected by the highest penalty for its destruction.

The Seventh Commandment
Deuteronomy 5:18

"You shall not commit adultery." As idolatry breaks the spiritual covenant with God, adultery breaks the marriage covenant with a spouse. Throughout the Scriptures there is much that warns against impurity in thought, word and deed. Jesus Himself gave warning against this sin of adultery and fornication. Scripture teaches purity in all relations of the sexes, the control of passion, and the reverence for marriage. Modern society needs to know how much God hates these sins of the flesh and to be reminded of the destruction that always follows in their wake. We need to guard our senses. Temptation can come in so many forms—books, movies, art, social and work situations, et cetera. We live in a sex-obsessed society, but God has not changed. He still requires sexual purity from His children. Like dishonoring parents, unfaithfulness to a spouse breaks down the foundations of society-at-large, affecting many lives, and so it is a very serious sin.

As idolatry breaks the spiritual covenant with God, adultery breaks the marriage covenant with a spouse.

The Eighth Commandment
Deuteronomy 5:19

"You shall not steal." This commandment concerns personal property. God gave the right to own material things to His people. We are called to share when necessary and serve one another as God's stewards, but

no other person has the right to take possessions from another without permission. Since a steward must give account to the owner, he must have the right to control what is put into his care. This commandment was expanded by other laws to forbid bribery, withholding of other men's wages, defrauding or deceiving, oppression, or violence to extract property or money.

The Ninth Commandment
Deuteronomy 5:20

As adultery is a deceitful break in the marriage covenant, lying words break down relationships among people in general. *"You shall not bear false witness against your neighbor."* This commandment had to do with lying and gossiping about any person, not just those living near us. In Matthew 22:39 Jesus said we were to love our "neighbors" as ourselves. If we truly loved people with Christ's love, we would not give in to selfish or Satanic temptations to "put them down" in an effort to raise up ourselves or our interests. The tongue is a little member, but *"how great a forest a little fire kindles!"* (James 3:5). This commandment is clear and direct. If something is not true, do not act or speak as if it were.

The Tenth Commandment
Deuteronomy 5:20

"You shall not covet." The keeping of this commandment affects both the inner and the outer man. Wrong desires most often will result in wrong actions. *"When desire has conceived, it gives birth to sin; and sin, when it is full-grown, brings forth death"* (James 1:15). And in Proverbs 23:7, *"As a man thinks in his heart, so is he."* In the Sermon on the Mount, Jesus showed the connection between the angry temper and the act of murder; the lustful glance and the broken vow of marriage. This is the teaching of the tenth commandment: stop the mental process of coveting by "changing channels" to God's frequency of praise, purity, thanksgiving, and truth. When the coveting stops, the sinful actions will stop also.

Ten Commandments— Not Suggestions!

How much better our world would be if we would take the time to understand and ask God's help in keeping these ten wonderful commandments! Without God, such obedience is impossible, but with Him, we can love Him "back" while loving all those around us. Have you ever taken time to memorize all ten for yourself, in order? It's never too late. Then pray and look for an opportunity to teach them to someone else.

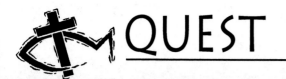 QUEST

LESSON 21

Questions

Study Procedure: Read the Scripture references before answering questions. Unless otherwise instructed, use the Bible only in answering questions. Some questions may be more difficult than others but try to answer as many as you can. Pray for God's wisdom and understanding as you study and don't be discouraged if some answers are not obvious at first. Do not read the study notes for this lesson until AFTER you have completed your questions.

Day One:

MEMORY: DEUTERONOMY 10:18

Write the Ten Commandments in order below. (Try not to peek at your notes!)

1. _____
2. _____
3. _____
4. _____
5. _____
6. _____
7. _____
8. _____
9. _____
10. _____

Place the number of each of the Ten Commandments listed above beneath the appropriate summary of them that Jesus used:

11. *"Love the LORD your God with all your heart, with all your soul, with all your strength, and with all your mind."* _____

12. *"Love your neighbor as yourself."* _____

Day Two: Read Deuteronomy 11

MEMORY: DEUTERONOMY 11:11-12

1. How did they get water for their land in Egypt, and how were they to get water for their crops in their new land? _____

_____

_____

_____

2. From verse 24, give the boundaries of the Promised Land. _____

_____

_____

3. Read Deuteronomy 12. How many places of worship were they to have in their new land?

_____

4. What group of people were they to be careful not to neglect?

    a) children

    b) Levites

    c) elderly

5. a) What verses mentioned that blood was not to be eaten? _____

    b) What reason was given for this? _____

Day Three:

MEMORY: DEUTERONOMY 14:2

1. From Deuteronomy 13, what was the punishment if someone or some group was found to be guilty of trying to lead others into false worship?

    a) death by stoning

    b) banishment from tribe

    c) to be sold as slaves

2. From Deuteronomy 14:1-2, what is the reason given for not disfiguring your body in any way?

_____

_____

_____

3. Read Deuteronomy 14:3-21. Give the characteristics of the land animals, fish, and birds that could be eaten:

    a) Deuteronomy 14:6 _____

    b) Deuteronomy 14:9 _____

    c) Deuteronomy 14:11 _____

4. From Deuteronomy 15:1-6 give God's unusual financial plan for Israel. _____

_____

_____

_____

5. From Deuteronomy 15:12-18, what was done to a slave who did not want his freedom?

_____

_____

Day Four:

1. Read Deuteronomy 16 and fill in the blanks with the following:

MEMORY: DEUTERONOMY 20:4

   Feast of Weeks   Feast of Tabernacles   Passover

   a) Observed in month of Abib; only unleavened bread eaten; reminder of the exodus from Egypt. _____

   b) Seven weeks after the first harvest, bring a gift in gratitude to God to the central place of worship. _____

   c) After all the harvests are over, this feast is celebrated for seven days. _____
   _____

2. Read Deuteronomy 17. From verses 6 and 7, what are the responsibilities of witnesses to a death penalty case? _____
   _____

3. Read Deuteronomy 18. What wicked customs of the people in the new land were to be avoided by Israel?_____
   _____
   _____

4. Who is the Prophet about whom Moses was speaking in verses 15, 18, and 19? _____

5. From Deuteronomy 18:21 and 22, what was the test of a true prophet of God? _____
   _____

Day Five: Read Deuteronomy 19 and 20

Circle the answer that best completes the following sentences.

1. The cities of refuge were
   a) vacation spots for tired Hebrew soldiers.
   b) public areas set aside for garbage collection.
   c) cities where a person accused of killing another accidentally could go to avoid the revenge of the family of the slain person.

2. It was against the law to remove a person's
   a) birthmark.
   b) landmark.
   c) hallmark.

3. The number of witnesses needed to establish the truth in a case was

    a) one.

    b) two or three.

    c) twelve.

4. The meaning of "eye for eye, tooth for tooth, hand for hand" was

    a) "the punishment must fit the crime."

    b) "take one of these, since everyone has another."

    c) "do the crime, do the time."

5. Which of the following could get a man out of military service?

    a) owning a new house that had not been dedicated

    b) owning a vineyard of which he had not yet tasted the grapes

    c) engaged to a wife but not yet married

    d) fear of fighting

    e) all of the above

6. Now take a few minutes to read your study notes for this lesson.

Notes

New Land, New Laws

What to Expect in the New Land
Deuteronomy 11

With every season, they could realize the blessings of obedience when the rains arrived, or be reminded of their sin and rebellion, when the rains came not.

Things would be different in Canaan. Egypt had been a place of rich farm land, irrigated generously with systems operated by a simple movement of a farmer's foot (Deuteronomy 11:10). In Canaan, Israel would have to depend on God for the rain needed to make the crops blossom and bear fruit. With every season, they could realize the blessings of obedience when the rains arrived, or be reminded of their sin and rebellion, when the rains came not. God had picked a land for His people that would require them to trust and obey Him if they were to succeed in it.

The boundaries promised in verses 23-25 included about 300,000 square miles of land, but sadly Israel never realized its full potential, only occupying 1/10th of the land promised (about 30,000 square miles) at the height of its power. How much like the New Testament promises to Christians! What a small amount of our blessings we ever actually enjoy because we will not respond obediently to what our Lord requires or because we dare put other things ahead of our devotion to Him!

One Place to Worship
Deuteronomy 12

The Lord required that Israel use only one central location for worship. He did not want them to act like the heathen people around them and have sacred spots on every hill. He was training them through this that the one central place of worship pointed to the bigger truth we know today: one central Person to worship, the Lord God Almighty.

False Prophets Not Tolerated
Deuteronomy 13

Israel was supposed to stay informed and aware of God's laws. If any person acted in a way that would lead people away from God's laws, even if that person demonstrated unusual powers, the person was not to be followed. Any person, group, or city that promoted false worship was to be thoroughly investigated, and if found guilty, executed. God wanted His people to actively oppose false teaching, not sit quietly by, letting it go on unchallenged. It would not take many stonings for false religions to die for lack of followers.

If any person acted in a way that would lead people away from God's laws, even if that person demonstrated unusual powers, the person was not to be followed.

Health Rules for Holy People
Deuteronomy 14

Because God valued His people so much, He did not want them cutting up or disfiguring themselves in any way, for any reason, as the heathen did. He also wanted them to be careful about what foods they ate. Three general categories of food were allowed: among the land animals, the kinds that had split hooves and chewed the cud; among fish, the kinds that had fins and scales; and among birds, any that were not **scavengers**, eating dead bodies. For their spiritual health, God required that they bring a tithe or a tenth of their crops as an offering to Him to support the ongoing work associated with worship.

scavengers - animals that feed on dead animals' flesh or other decaying matter

Three Trips Per Year
Deuteronomy 15

All able-bodied men in Israel were to travel to the central place of worship to offer sacrifices and celebrate feasts of thanksgiving for God's protection and love toward them. The three trips included a celebration of Passover and Unleavened Bread for seven days in the month of Abib; seven weeks later the Feast of Weeks or Pentecost (fifty days) in gratitude for the continuing harvest; and finally, in the fall, after the harvests were over, a celebration of the Feast of Tabernacles. This chapter also included directions for selection of judges and city officials for each city's government (Deuteronomy 16:18).

More Laws
Deuteronomy 17

Offerings to God were to represent the best a person had, not the least or the **expendable**. The motive of the giver, then as now, was important to God (Deuteronomy 17:1). The death penalty was ordered as the appropriate penalty for the sin of idolatry. After careful investigation, if found guilty, a person was to be executed by stoning, and thus, that sin was stopped. How many would be alive today if

expendable - non-essential

We should be grateful for the forgiving mercies of our God toward us, and voluntarily examine ourselves to root out all idolatry.

the death penalty were given to all who put other things ahead of their love for God? We should be grateful for the forgiving mercies of our God toward us, and voluntarily examine ourselves to root out all idolatry. It is still the sin that causes most of the problems in any nation.

About Witnesses

An important rule of law is found in Deuteronomy 17:6: *"Whoever is deserving of death shall be put to death on the testimony of two or three witnesses; he shall not be put to death on the testimony of one witness."* More than one witness was considered necessary to establish the truth about a matter; this law is still true in courts today.

About Kings

God knew that in the future, Israel would want a king like other countries had. So, ahead of time, God set some standards. Israel's king was not to have a large number of horses because he was to depend on God for protection, not on great military might. Next, Israel's king was not to have many wives since they would certainly turn his heart away from the Lord. Thirdly, Israel's king was not to try to acquire great amounts of silver and gold because that, too, would turn his attention away from God as the true source for what Israel needed. David's son Solomon violated all these standards and hurt greatly the future of Israel as a world power. On the positive side, the king of Israel was to be a man who knew and loved the Word of God. He was to have his own copy and read it daily.

Priests and Prophets
Deuteronomy 18

The tribe of Levi had been selected by God to spend their lives in His service. They were not to own land or have other jobs, but were to be supported by the offerings of the other tribes so that they would be free to do what the Lord required. God's workers in ministry should be supported by those served by their ministry. Canaan was full of people who practiced false religions. Israel was warned not to participate in any of their **occult** activities. Some named that we still hear about in the world are human sacrifice, divination, reading of horoscopes, witchcraft, contacting evil spirits or spirits of the dead. God said bluntly that He hated all such practices. It is shocking today to see how many Christians think such practices are humorous or harmless and encourage their observance at Halloween or other carnival activities. God's opinion of these and other forms of idolatry remains the same: He hates them.

occult - pertaining to supernatural influences, agencies, or phenomena

The Prophet

Moses included in Deuteronomy 18 a prophecy that would be taught to every Jewish generation: the coming of a great Prophet—even greater than Moses had been. Of course, that Prophet was our own Jesus. That is why in the gospels there are several instances in which Jesus was asked if He were "that Prophet" (John 1:21, John 6:14).

Perfect Prophets

God gave a test for determining whether someone was a true prophet of God or not. What was the test? They were to be 100% accurate in what they predicted! 100% seems very high, yet God is God and He is never wrong. If He tells His prophets something, He will make it happen. If the prophecy fails, it was not of God and the prophet was a false one, deserving capital punishment. Not many would dare apply for that job!

God gave a test for determining whether someone was a true prophet of God or not. What was the test? They were to be 100% accurate in what they predicted!

Places to Escape
Deuteronomy 19

God had a real compassion for someone falsely accused of murder. He provided for cities of refuge to be set aside for the purpose of protecting someone who unintentionally caused the death of another. Without such a place, a person could be the victim of a **bereaved** family's revenge before a fair trial had been conducted. God did not offer such protection to a murderer who knowingly and purposely ended the life of another. That one was sentenced to death. God also recognized that some people cheated others and issued a law against trying to change someone's property lines for another's advantage. Fairness or justice is an important attribute of God, which made Him different from the gods of the heathen. He ordered that the penalties for crimes should be in keeping with the seriousness of the crimes committed. In Deuteronomy 19:21 we found the famous quotation *"eye for eye, tooth for tooth"* which was much more merciful than the heathen policy of revenge in excess of any wrong done. The punishment was to fit the crime.

bereaved - suffering or mourning the death of a loved one

Rules of War
Deuteronomy 20

God had an interesting attitude toward those serving in the military; He wanted whole-hearted soldiers. So, if a man were distracted by any of the following situations, he could be excused: the completion of a new house that had not yet been dedicated; ownership of a new vineyard, the grapes of which had not been tasted; betrothal to a woman with the marriage not yet **consummated**; or an overwhelming fear about the upcoming battle. (See Judges 7:3 for an interesting application of this.)

consummated - to fulfill a marriage with the first act of sexual intercourse after the ceremony

God also outlined methods for seeking peace first with neighboring cities before starting to fight. If peace was refused, then they were to follow the other procedures given in regard to warfare and destruction of property. Israel was not to be afraid when led by God into war: *"for the Lord your God is He who goes with you, to fight for you against your enemies, to save you"* (Deuteronomy 20:4).

When you need direction for your daily life, search out His will on the matter through prayer and Bible study.

Summary These lessons are designed to help the student survey the wide range of laws God gave Israel. New Testament Christians are not bound to keep all these laws, but there are general principles that, if applied to modern life, would still greatly improve our societies. At least it should be encouraging for us to see how detailed God's concern was for every area of Israel's life. He is just as concerned with every area of your life today. When you need direction for your daily life, search out His will on the matter through prayer and Bible study. You will not fail when you are led by His Spirit.

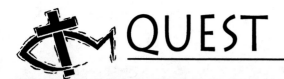 QUEST

Questions

Study Procedure: Read the Scripture references before answering questions. Unless otherwise instructed, use the Bible only in answering questions. Some questions may be more difficult than others but try to answer as many as you can. Pray for God's wisdom and understanding as you study and don't be discouraged if some answers are not obvious at first. Do not read the study notes for this lesson until AFTER you have completed your questions.

Day One:

MEMORY: LUKE 4:8

I. Vocabulary Matching

_____1. expendable   a) unholy spiritual activity

_____2. occult   b) eaters of dead flesh

_____3. scavengers   c) suffered loss

_____4. bereaved   d) finalize as in a wedding

_____5. consummate   e) unnecessary

II. Review of Deuteronomy 11-20: Matching

_____1. watery borders of Israel   a) executed by stoning

_____2. forbidden   b) buzzard

_____3. false prophets   c) chosen to serve God

_____4. scavenger   d) eating of blood

_____5. Levites   e) Jesus

_____6. The Prophet   f) Mediterranean and Euphrates

Day Two:

1. Read Deuteronomy 21. In 21:1-9 God gave directions for investigating a murder. If the guilty party could not be found, what ceremony was to be performed and why? _____

_____

_____

_____

_____

_____

2. How does our society react to the taking of life today? _____

_____

_____

_____

3. Pick one of the following laws and comment on what you find interesting about it.

Female Captives (verses 10-14); Firstborn Inheritance Rights (verses 15-17); Rebellious Son (verses 18-21) _____

_____

_____

4. Read Deuteronomy 22. This includes several very interesting and unusual laws. Pick out one or two and try to discover God's purpose for issuing them. Write your discoveries below and share with your group. _____

_____

_____

_____

_____

Day Three: Read Deuteronomy 23   *MEMORY: DEUTERONOMY 23:21*

1. The Lord has a long memory about which of the following in verses 1-8:

    a) cheating

    b) illegitimacy

    c) failure to show hospitality

    d) gossip

    e) family relationships

2. Read Deuteronomy 23:9-14. With what is God concerned in the camp? _____

3. From verses 15-24, summarize God's laws about the following:

    a) male and female prostitutes _____

    _____

    b) escaped slaves _____

    _____

    c) interest_____

    _____

    d) vows _____

    _____

    e) eating from your neighbor's farm plot _____

    _____

    _____

4. Read Deuteronomy 24 and give the verses where these are discussed.

    a) kidnappers _____

    b) rights of the borrower _____

    c) provision for the needy _____

Day Four: Read Deuteronomy 25

1. How did the law of Deuteronomy 25:1-4 guard against extreme punishment? _____

_____

2. Compare Deuteronomy 25:5-10 with Ruth 4:1-12. How did Boaz follow the law in his transaction regarding Ruth? What did he omit, if anything? _____

_____

_____

_____

_____

3. Read Deuteronomy 26. How did God insure with the ceremony described here that the history of Israel would be taught to every man? _____

_____

_____

_____

4. Read Deuteronomy 27. This introduces the blessings and cursings of Deuteronomy 28-30. Half of Israel was to stand on one mountain and half on the other to hear again the words of the law and the results of obedience or disobedience. List the tribes that would stand on each of the mountains below:

    a) Gerizim _____

    b) Ebal _____

MEMORY: DEUTERONOMY 28:1, 29:5

Day Five: Read Deuteronomy 28-30

1. To receive the blessings from God, Israel was to obey_____and to observe

_____ His commandments. (Use adverbs.)

2. What verses in Chapter 28 described the

    a) blessings of obedience?_____

    b) penalties for disobedience?_____

3. Deuteronomy 28:48 seems to summarize the worst of all the curses. Consider how it describes Christ's condition on the cross. Write out any thoughts you have on this.

_____

_____

_____

4. Chapter 29 reviews the covenant God made with Israel. From verse 9, what must Israel do to prosper? _____

5. In Chapter 30, Moses uses powerful opposites to make his point. What did the following illustrate?

　　a) in heaven or beyond the sea—near you, in your mouth _____

　　　_____

　　b) life and good, death and evil _____

　　　_____

　　c) blessing and cursing _____

　　　_____

　　d) heaven and earth _____

　　　_____

6. Now take a few minutes to read your study notes for this lesson.

Notes

God's Laws for Right Living

Unsolved Murders
Deuteronomy 21:1-9

God said a community was responsible for the crimes committed within its boundaries. The spiritual principle here should make us take notice.

Ever since Chapter 8 of Deuteronomy, we have had a steady flow of laws for the nation of Israel as a whole. Deuteronomy Chapter 21 is the last of these listings. The focus of the first section (Deuteronomy 21:1-9) was the procedures to be followed in an unsolved murder. Interestingly, God said that the city determined to be closest to the site of the murder had a responsibility for the investigation. If no murderer was found, the whole city assumed the guilt for it and had to sacrifice a heifer and confess over it, *"Provide atonement, O Lord, for Your people Israel, whom You have redeemed, and do not lay innocent blood to the charge of Your people Israel."* The passage added, *"And atonement shall be provided on their behalf for the blood."* What a concept! God said a community was responsible for the crimes committed within its boundaries. The spiritual principle here should make us take notice. We cannot sit idly by and hear and forget the evening news about our communities. We must be active in "solving" the problems, and if unsuccessful, we must pray for our communities and repent of our corporate sins. How our cities might change if more Christians accepted the spiritual responsibility for intercession, involvement, and intense interest in local actions! Fewer violent crimes, fewer abortions, and fewer people paralyzed by fear would certainly result.

Captured Slaves, Second Wives, and Stubborn Sons
Deuteronomy 21:10-21

During war if a woman was captured and brought home as a wife and later disliked, God did not allow her to be mistreated. Another domestic problem of that day was multiple wives. A second wife and her children (this is a problem in our day, too, with rampant divorce) might be loved by the husband more than the original wife and her children. God's law did not allow a man to change the inheritance to suit his changing emotions. The firstborn of the first wife was to receive the proper inheritance. The third issue concerned dealing with a rebellious son. When the parents had exhausted all means of restraining and correcting such a son, they could appeal to the city elders, who would execute the son in order to stop such behavior from taking over the community. This is a shocking practice to us, but certainly it would have been a last resort and not needed very frequently. One such death would have shaped up many delinquent sons! When Jesus told the story of the prodigal son in Luke 15, His listeners might have expected it to end, according to law, in the death of that son, but in demonstration of God's love and mercy, Jesus had the son return and receive full forgiveness and family rights. Aren't we grateful for the mercy of God toward us!

When the parents had exhausted all means of restraining and correcting such a son, they could appeal to the city elders, who would execute the son in order to stop such behavior from taking over the community.

Hanging from a Tree
Deuteronomy 21:22-23

The final section of this chapter was important because Paul referred to it when explaining the meaning of Christ's death. The law read that any person hanged on a tree as a spectacle after execution must be taken down by nightfall and buried as a matter of decency. However, such a person was accursed by God. Paul wrote that Jesus, "hanged" on a tree by crucifixion became a curse or took on our curse for us so that we did not have to be judged for it (Galatians 3:13).

Personal Problems Addressed
Deuteronomy 22

This chapter began a different section of laws. From Chapter 22 through 26 Moses recorded God's directions for applying the law in personal situations. Again, we need to remember that we are no longer bound to follow all these laws, but we can still learn from the wisdom in their underlying principles. First, in this section, God wanted His people to show genuine concern for the needs of others. If a neighbor's livestock was out of its usual boundaries, the one seeing it was warned not to "hide" himself from the work needed to help his neighbor. How often do we "duck" our responsibilities to show love to others because of the energy or time needed to get involved? Secondly, a brief law ordered that men and women should not "cross-dress" (a man wearing a woman's clothing or a woman wearing a man's). Blurring sexual identity is still not emotionally or spiritually healthy. From verses 6 through 30 a wide variety of subjects were addressed: kindness to birds (verses 6-7); safety railings for roofs (verse 8); avoidance of mixtures (verses 9-11); identifying tassels on men's garments (verse 12); fairness to a wife accused of impurity (verses 13-21); adultery and rape (verses 22-29); and incest (verse 30).

How often do we "duck" our responsibilities to show love to others because of the energy or time needed to get involved?

Disqualified from Fellowship
Deuteronomy 23:1-11

From time to time the whole nation of Israel was called together as a "congregation" or "assembly" for special training, worship, or correction. This chapter lists those not allowed to join such an assembly. Men who had been castrated or people of illegitimate birth were not to be included. Both situations resulted because of heathen influence and violated God's holy standard. Later on there would be exceptions to this law, depending on the character of an individual, but at the beginning of this nation's history, the law was quite strict. (See Isaiah 56:3-8 and Acts 8:27,38 for God's mercy to these groups.) Ammonites and Moabites were long-time enemies of Israel and were also excluded from the congregation of Israel. Edomites, however, because of their relationship to Israel (Edom or Esau was the brother of Jacob), were to be included in the fellowship. Egyptians, also, could be accepted since they had hosted Israel for many years.

Cleanliness, Kindness, Purity, Truth, and Sharing
Deuteronomy 23:12-25

Our modern society issues much legislation insuring proper sanitation for cities, but God invented the idea. In Deuteronomy 23:12-13 Moses recorded the instructions for latrine areas outside the camp. Next, a law was given offering protection for runaway slaves. Specific laws against prostitution by women or men were given. No money made from female prostitutes (harlots) or male prostitutes (dogs) was ever to be used in the Lord's work. This issue comes up in our day when schools or other groups debate whether or not to receive gifts or grants of money from organizations which profit from harmful activities such as liquor, tobacco, or gambling sales. The principle in this passage would indicate that such gifts were not to be accepted. Loans were to be made to relatives without interest, but interest (usury) could be charged to foreigners receiving loans. Another law followed about the importance of keeping any vow voluntarily made to God. The final law in this very miscellaneous group dealt with "snacking" from your neighbor's garden plot. Satisfying immediate hunger was acceptable, but no gathering for later use was allowed.

Divorce
Deuteronomy
24:1-4

When the law in these verses was read, you probably noticed how simple it was for a husband to divorce his wife. We grieve over the frequency of divorce in our day because of the devastation it always causes to those touched by it. However, in Israel's development as a nation things were bad, too. By the time Jesus came down to us on earth, the Pharisees had interpreted Moses' original law to include the husband's right to divorce his wife for literally anything—even if she just scorched his soup! Matthew recorded Jesus' response to this problem in Matthew 19:4-9: *"Have you not read that He who made them at the beginning 'made them male and female', and said, 'For this reason a man shall leave his father and mother and be joined to his wife, and the two shall become one flesh'? So then, they are no longer two but one flesh. Therefore what God has joined together, let not man separate.... Moses, because of the hardness of your hearts, permitted you to divorce your wives, but from the beginning it was not so. And I say to you, whoever divorces his wife, except for sexual immorality, and marries another, commits adultery; and whoever marries her who is divorced commits adultery."* Divorce, instead of abuse or abandonment, was allowed to give mercy where hard-hearted spouses were involved. A focus of prayer for troubled marriages should be, then, that God would soften the hearts of the couple toward Him and toward each other. Tender-hearted people do not need divorce.

A focus of prayer for troubled marriages should be, then, that God would soften the hearts of the couple toward Him and toward each other. Tender-hearted people do not need divorce.

More and
Various Laws
Deuteronomy
24:5-22

A man newly married was to be granted an exemption from military service (verse 5). If a man loaned money to another, he was not allowed to take the millstone, by which a person made his living, as collateral for the loan (verse 6). Changing subjects again, kidnapping was a capital offense, and outbreaks of leprosy were to be treated carefully (verses 7-9). Kindness was to be shown to those owing money to another. Their privacy was not to be invaded just because they were indebted to someone (verses 10-13). In the same way, a poor servant was to be paid regularly and quickly and not abused because of his vulnerable position (verses 14-15). Punishment for sin was to be received individually; other family members were not to be punished for another one's sin (verse 16). Foreigners, orphans, and widows were to be treated mercifully because that situation could befall anyone (verses 17-18). For the homeless or poor, God designed a "workfare" program in which farmers did not pick their vines or fields clean but purposely left some to be harvested by the needy (verses 19-22). In all these laws, God's eternal concern for the needs of the

In all these laws, God's eternal concern for the needs of the individual was emphasized. Those who were blessed materially were to share with those who were not, either directly by gifts or indirectly by offering work for fair wages.

individual was emphasized. Those who were blessed materially were to share with those who were not, either directly by gifts or indirectly by offering work for fair wages. We could apply many of these principles to our present systems of help and bring to them great improvement.

Public Punishment, Kindness to Animals
Deuteronomy 25

Again in this chapter there was no unifying theme, just a series of interesting but unrelated legislation. First, in cases where less-serious crimes were committed, the punishment would be a certain number of "stripes" or "blows" from a whip. The judge was to witness the punishment to assure that it was not overdone, and no man was to receive more than forty in all. The next law stated that the ox used to tread out the grain was not to be muzzled but allowed to eat occasionally from the results of the work he had done. This was later quoted in the New Testament as a precedent for paying the preachers: *"Even so the Lord has commanded that those who preach the gospel should live from the gospel"* (1 Corinthians 9:14).

Kinsman Redeemer
Deuteronomy 25:5-10

A unique piece of legislation came next. It was known as the "Law of the Kinsman Redeemer" and was designed to protect widows. If a woman's husband died before they had had a son, she was to marry a near relative of her husband so that any land holdings would remain in that family, protecting the inheritance of the tribe, and also so that she would be guaranteed protection and provision after her husband's death. Any child born to the second union would legally be considered the child of her dead husband, so that his name would not be lost from the family genealogy. There were three conditions to be met in this second marriage so that no one was forced into anything. First, the new choice for husband had to be the nearest relative or kinsman to the deceased husband. Secondly, he had to be financially able to make this new commitment, and finally, he had to be willing to marry the widow. If he was not willing, he could refuse and the next relative could be approached. This matter was handled publicly and legally in the place for such business, in front of the city elders. It was considered a disgrace if a man refused to do his duty to a widow, and she could show her disgust by spitting in his face and removing his sandal. The removal of the sandal was a covenant "picture" that the man had refused to walk in the shoes of his brother to do the right thing. In Chapter 4 of the book of Ruth this law was used dramatically. There however, Boaz, a wealthy kinsman of Ruth's dead husband, wanted to marry her, but a nearer kinsman had the first rights. Boaz approached him in front of the elders, but when he refused to take Ruth as wife, Boaz took his sandal, symbolizing that he would walk in his place, and was free to marry Ruth. Even greater than that happy ending was that Jesus became our Kinsman Redeemer. He put on flesh to become our Kinsman, defeated our relative Satan, who had the prior claim, and was willing and able to "marry" us, taking us into His home and caring for us forever. What a wonderful plan!

Jesus became our Kinsman Redeemer. He put on flesh to become our Kinsman, defeated our relative Satan, who had the prior claim, and was willing and able to "marry" us, taking us into His home and caring for us forever. What a wonderful plan!

Danger of Interfering, Honesty, Revenge
Deuteronomy 25:11-19

If a woman interfered in a fight between two men and hurt one in his private area, she faced the punishment of having her hand cut off! Evidently, this law kept women out of such matters. Honesty among merchants was ordered (verses 11,12). No one was to have double sets of weights—differing from each other to the merchant's advantage (verses 13-16). The final law of this chapter revealed God's plan for the destruction of the Amalekites because of their long-term rebellion against Him and cruelty to Israel (verses 17-19).

A Real Thanksgiving at First Fruits
Deuteronomy 26

One of the seven holy festivals during the year that able-bodied men were required to attend was the Feast of First Fruits. The "first fruits" were the earliest crops that were harvested in the spring. A portion of this harvest was to be taken to the central place of worship and offered to the Lord. The one bringing the offering approached the priest and recited a memorized summary of God's wonderful help to Israel as a people, ending with these words: *"Behold, I have brought the firstfruits of the land which you, O Lord, have given me"* (Deuteronomy 26:10). In preparation for this feast, then, the history of Israel was taught and remembered by many, and minds were filled again with appreciation for the Lord of their harvest.

Last Minute Preparations
Deuteronomy 27

Israel, in Chapters 27-30, was just about ready to enter Canaan. Moses described to them the preparations necessary for the ceremony that would be held when they crossed over. Permanent stone tablets, whitewashed and inscribed with the words of the Law, were to be prepared and placed on Mt. Ebal. Mt. Ebal and Mt. Gerizim joined at a valley that formed a wonderful natural amphitheater. Half of Israel on each mountain slope would gather to hear the words of the law read, witness the sacrifices offered on the new altar built below, and worship the Lord, who had brought them to this new land. Moses listed in verses 14 through 26 the curses that would result from a failure to obey God. The Levites were to read them, and the people were to respond to each with "Amen!"

The covenant offered to Israel in this chapter was conditional and temporary. If Israel obeyed God's commandments, He would allow her to remain in the land; if she disobeyed, which she did later on, she would be removed from the land.

The Covenant Renewed
Deuteronomy 28, 29, 30

Abraham had been part of an unconditional or permanent covenant with God whereby God promised him a great name, a great family, covenant protection, and permanent ownership of a new land. The covenant offered to Israel in this chapter was conditional and temporary. If Israel obeyed God's commandments, He would allow her to remain in the land; if she disobeyed, which she did later on, she would be removed from the land. Because of God's unconditional covenant with Abraham, the land of Canaan would always belong to Israel. God would bring back to that land whatever remnant of Israel would come to Him in faith. God's will was and is perfect; Israel would be blessed if she obeyed it and cursed if she disobeyed it. The list of blessings and curses are not hard to understand. One could trace the history of Israel and find specific fulfillments of the curses that fell on her because of repeated disobedience.

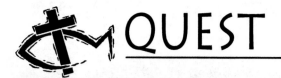

QUEST

Questions

Study Procedure: Read the Scripture references before answering questions. Unless otherwise instructed, use the Bible only in answering questions. Some questions may be more difficult than others but try to answer as many as you can. Pray for God's wisdom and understanding as you study and don't be discouraged if some answers are not obvious at first. Do not read the study notes for this lesson until AFTER you have completed your questions.

MAP STUDY

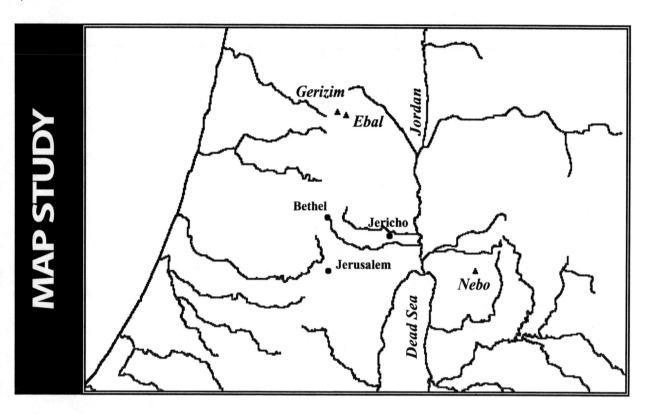

Day One:

1. Locate on the map Mt. Ebal and Mt. Gerizim on which the children of Israel stood as Moses proclaimed the curses and blessings.

2. As you think about the laws that were instituted in Deuteronomy 21-30, choose at least three laws and contrast or compare them with laws in our current judicial system. _____

    _____

    _____

    _____

    _____

    _____

    _____

    _____

Day Two:

1. Read Deuteronomy 31 and 34:7. How old

    was Moses? _____

   MEMORY: DEUTERONOMY 31:6

2. What reason(s) did Moses give for the change of leadership that was to occur? _____

    _____

    _____

3. Copy down the powerful words of verse 8 which show why Joshua could be of "good courage."

    _____

    _____

4. From Deuteronomy 31:9-24, find two things that Moses wrote and give the purpose for each.

    _____

    _____

    _____

    _____

    _____

Day Three: Read Deuteronomy 32

Find the verses that match these summaries from the Song of Moses.

1. Let these words sink in to nourish and cleanse you. _____

2. God is our Rock (our Sure Foundation, our Strong One, our High Place). _____

3. You are rebellious children. Your Father should not be treated like this by you! _____

4. Remember all God has done to protect you and provide for you. _____

5. With no good reason, Israel sinned against God and turned to idols. _____

6. God will not ignore such rebellion but will certainly punish it. _____

7. They aren't thinking! How could they have gotten this far without their Rock? Their false gods

    are not good like our God. _____

8. Judgment will surely come: vengeance on His enemies, help for His people. _____

Day Four: Read Deuteronomy 33

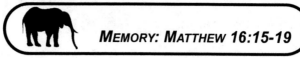

MEMORY: MATTHEW 16:15-19

1. From verse 2, what new detail is revealed about the giving of the law on Sinai?

_____

2. a) Which tribe is omitted here? (See Genesis 49:5-7.) _____

   b) Did it get an inheritance? Explain. (See Joshua 19:2-9.) _____

_____

_____

_____

3. What are Thummim and Urim in verse 8? (Use a Bible dictionary or footnotes for this.)

_____

_____

_____

_____

4. Write out at least one favorite verse from this chapter. _____

_____

_____

Day Five: Read Deuteronomy 34

MEMORY: 3 JOHN 11

1. At 120, what still "worked" for Moses?

_____

2. Read Jude 9 and compare it to Deuteronomy 34:6. Who buried Moses, and why do you think it was handled this way? _____

_____

_____

_____

3. Give a few examples from the life of Moses that have caused you to examine or improve your own service for God. _____

_____

_____

4. Now take a few minutes to read your study notes for this lesson.

Notes

Last Days of Moses

So far this year we have followed Israel out of Egypt and then watched anxiously as God worked "Egypt" out of Israel!

The Last Days of Moses
Deuteronomy 31-34

This is the final lesson on Deuteronomy and with it will come a study of the last days of Moses on this earth and the last days of Israel in the wilderness. So far this year we have followed Israel out of Egypt and then watched anxiously as God worked "Egypt" out of Israel! They had learned many things about God and about themselves, and, hopefully, so have we. Next week starts the last section of this year's survey, "The Conquest of Canaan." It, too, will provide much opportunity for spiritual exploration and discovery.

Moses Announces Change of Leaders
Deuteronomy 31:1-8

Always right to the point, Moses announced the change of leadership from himself to Joshua. God had decided it, so there was no need to debate or complain. Then, Moses, known to his people for his clear delivery of God's Word, went on to reveal a sure prophecy for their future: *"The Lord your God Himself crosses over before you; He will destroy these nations from before you, and you shall dispossess them. Joshua himself crosses over before you, just as the Lord has said"* (Deuteronomy 31:3). Moses was a model for how leadership changes should occur. First, he had accepted, though sad at missing the future challenges, God's will in the timing of his own death. Second, he encouraged the people about the change of leaders, pointing them to their ever-faithful Heavenly Guide, God Himself. Third, he "built up" Joshua before the people as God's able choice, instead of drawing attention to how they would miss him and his forty-years' experience. And finally, he personally encouraged Joshua, who had served Moses faithfully since the law was given on Mt. Sinai forty years before. We should learn from this transition. When we are serving the Lord properly, we should be able to step down without hindering the on-going effectiveness of the Lord's work. Moses had served well.

When we are serving the Lord properly, we should be able to step down without hindering the on-going effectiveness of the Lord's work.

The Law Entrusted to the Priests and Elders
Deuteronomy 31:9-30

After Moses had turned over his leadership of the nation and its army to Joshua, he turned to the priests and the elders and gave them the responsibility of keeping the copy of God's law which Scripture credited Moses with writing. This included the first five books of the Bible called the Pentateuch. The priests and elders were not only to protect the copy of the law (it was placed in the ark of the covenant for safekeeping during wartime) but also to see that it was read and understood at regular seven-year intervals. This public reading and explanation of the law did not take the place of the daily responsibility of the parents to teach it to their children. How wonderful it would be to systematically read the Bible aloud in our homes for devotions in the presence of our family, taking seven years to do it! Fathers are priests within their homes, and what an impact it makes when men take seriously their responsibility to know and teach God's Word, not leaving the spiritual welfare to be handled solely by their wives.

| **The Song of Moses**
Deuteronomy 32:1-52 | We do not have the tune, but the words are powerful to Moses' song! Remember his sister Miriam had led one herself when they crossed the Red Sea. How appropriate that when they crossed the Jordan into the Promised Land they would have this song of Moses to remind them |

of the awesome power of their God and their own weakness when they tried to live apart from His will! God commanded Moses to write it to be a *"witness for Me against the children of Israel."* God knew that Israel would soon fall back into their old independent ways and forsake the commands of the God who had saved them. He wanted Israel to have this record of His faithfulness hidden in their hearts so that His Spirit could bring it to their memories and quicken their hearts to repent and return.

This song of Moses is not out of date yet. In Revelation 15:3, it is stated that the song of Moses will be sung in heaven right along with the song of the Lamb. In it we have a contrast of the unchanging faithfulness of God with the future unfaithfulness of the people. Music is a powerful medium. Martin Luther, the great reformer, remarked that next to theology, music was the most important subject to study, because it too, had the power to move men's souls. There is room in our day for more Christian songwriters to communicate God's truths in memorable ways.

> *Martin Luther, the great reformer, remarked that next to theology, music was the most important subject to study, because it too, had the power to move men's souls.*

| **The Blessing of Moses**
Deuteronomy 33:1-29 | The children of Israel were challenged once more to obey consistently the Word of God. Moses said, *"For it is not a futile thing for you, because it is your life."* Before going to the top of Mount Nebo to take a view of the land he was not permitted to enter, he spoke a blessing on the tribes |

of Israel. In the previous song, Moses focused mostly on the judgments that would come upon the people when they turned away from God to idols or selfish pursuits in the future. But, in this blessing on them, he mentioned the benefits they would receive because of the Lord's never-ending mercy. The prophetic tribal blessings were Moses' farewell warnings and farewell benedictions to encourage them to choose to walk in the ways of God, their only true source of help and goodness. It would make an interesting but lengthy study in itself to trace the fulfillment of the blessings of Moses on the twelve tribes as they took up their assigned settlements in the Promised Land. Along with Moses' blessings should be paired the blessings of Jacob in Genesis 49 on the same tribes. The accuracy with which these prophetic blessings were fulfilled testifies to the omniscience and omnipotence of the Lord, who inspired Moses and Jacob to speak them.

An Encouraging Word
Deuteronomy 33:27

Our circumstances are under God's control, and He is able to match His supply to our need.

"The eternal God is your refuge, and underneath are the everlasting arms." This was a promise that God would graciously support His people through their troubles and trials wherever and whatever they were. It is one of the promises to Israel that the church can also confidently claim. Our circumstances are under God's control, and He is able to match His supply to our need. God is the refuge or dwelling place of His people and their protection through the storms of life. With these poetic blessings, Moses brought to an end his term of office as the commander-in-chief of Israel.

The Death of Moses
Deuteronomy 34:1-12

Dead prophets were often highly honored by Israel even though living ones were frequently ignored.

The account of the death and burial of Moses was probably added by Joshua to complete the history of Moses. From the top of Mt. Pisgah, Moses surveyed with his eyes the length and breadth of the Promised Land. Afterward, he died there, *"in the land of Moab, according to the word of the Lord."* As God would later announce to Joshua, *"Moses, My servant is dead."* God loved Moses and Moses loved God. As a leader, Moses was not exempt from careful obedience to the commands of God, but as a man, he was not completely willing at all times to submit to those commands. Scripture did not hide from us his imperfections. Yet, God honored Moses in a unique way on the day he died; the Scripture noted that God Himself buried him. The place and details were kept secret, probably so that Israel would not be tempted to worship their leader instead of their Lord. Dead prophets were often highly honored by Israel even though living ones were frequently ignored. The superb leadership of Moses would continue through God's newly chosen vessel, Joshua. The greatness of a leader can be seen in the effective work of those he has led. Joshua learned well from Moses' example and would prove to be a great credit to his teacher and his nation.

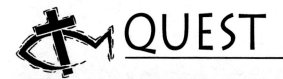 QUEST

LESSON 24

Questions

Study Procedure: Read the Scripture references before answering questions. Unless otherwise instructed, use the Bible only in answering questions. Some questions may be more difficult than others but try to answer as many as you can. Pray for God's wisdom and understanding as you study and don't be discouraged if some answers are not obvious at first. Do not read the study notes for this lesson until AFTER you have completed your questions.

Day One: Deuteronomy Review

1. Fill in the blanks with the tribes missing from this list. Reuben, Simeon, Levi, Judah, Issachar,

   Z _____, G _____, Asshur, D_____, Naphtali, Joseph

   (M_____ and E _____), Benjamin.

2. Jesus summarized all the commandments of God with two statements from Matthew 22: 37-40. Write them below. _____

   _____

   _____

   _____

3. Moses' Family Tree: Matching

   _____ a) father   1) Zipporah

   _____ b) mother   2) Miriam

   _____ c) sister   3) Jochebed

   _____ d) brother   4) Gershom

   _____ e) older don   5) Aaron

   _____ f) father-in-law   6) Amram

   _____ g) brother-in-law   7) Jethro

   _____ h) wife   8) Hobab

   _____ i) younger son   9) Eliezer

Day Two: Read Joshua 1

1. The worker dies but the work goes on. From verses 2-9, make a note of the encouragement

   MEMORY: JOSHUA 1:8-9

   God gave to Joshua as he assumed his new leadership position over Israel. _____

   _____

   _____

   _____

   _____

2. From Joshua 1:6-9 write out what results were assured if Joshua remained "strong and of good courage." _____

_____

_____

3. What lay between Israel's army and the land of Canaan? _____

4. What tribes received a specific reminder from Joshua about their duties and why?

_____

_____

_____

Day Three: Read Joshua 2

MEMORY: HABAKKUK 3:17-19

1. Why were two men sent out by Joshua?

_____

2. Why do you think they chose to enter Rahab's dwelling? _____

_____

_____

3. Why did Rahab hide them from the king of Jericho's men? _____

_____

_____

_____

4. With what specific events in Israel's history was Rahab familiar? _____

_____

Day Four:

1. What request of Rahab's revealed her faith in their God? _____

_____

_____

_____

2. For what two purposes was the scarlet rope used?_____

_____

3. What is the significance of the scarlet rope for us? _____

_____

_____

Day Five:

MEMORY: ZEPHANIAH 3:17

1. What was the report of the spies to Joshua?

_____

_____

2. How did this differ from the earlier report of the spies in Numbers 13? _____

_____

3. The New Testament refers to Rahab three times. Write out what is told of her in each of the references below:

a) Matthew 1:1-5 _____

_____

b) Hebrews 11:31 _____

_____

c) James 2:25 _____

_____

4. In your own words, write down anything we can learn from this episode. _____

_____

_____

_____

5. Now take a few minutes to read your study notes for this lesson.

Notes

Conquest of Canaan

Introduction to the Book of Joshua

Joshua started where Deuteronomy left off. Its account of Israel's early efforts under the new leadership of Joshua, following the death of Moses, has similarities to the book of Acts. Acts recorded the first activities of the early Church, under the leadership of the Holy Spirit, after the death and resurrection of Jesus. Similarly, the book of Joshua is full of miraculous displays of God's power on behalf of those who are strong in faith and of "good courage."

Joshua is full of miraculous displays of God's power on behalf of those who are strong in faith and of "good courage."

Who Wrote It? The authorities who lived nearest the time of Joshua, credited him with writing all but the account of his own death. As you read it yourself, watch for passages written in the first person, which indicate that an eye-witness was speaking: *"Until we had crossed over"* (Joshua 5:1), *"... the land which the Lord had sworn to their fathers that He would give us...."* (Joshua 5:6). Also statements like this one about Rahab: *"So she dwells in Israel to this day..."* (Joshua 6:25), give evidence that the record was written by someone living during the same period in which these incidences occurred. These and other details strengthen the traditional view which gives credit to Joshua as author.

How Is It Organized? The message of Joshua could be categorized this way:

1. Israel Enters Canaan and Conquers the Inhabitants (Joshua 1-12).
2. The Land Is Divided and Assigned to 10 1/2 Tribes (Joshua 13-22).
3. Joshua Delivers Final Messages to Israel Before His Death (Joshua 23-24).

Who Was Joshua? Joshua was a leader in the tribe of Ephraim. He had been born in Egypt and selected by Moses as his servant or attendant during his term as leader. Like Moses, Joshua had been thoroughly trained and tested before being given the top position. He probably was about eighty years old when he took over and served faithfully for nearly thirty years before his death at the age of one hundred and ten. Joshua's original name was Hoshea or Oshea but was evidently changed, perhaps by Moses, to Jehoshua, meaning Jehovah is Salvation (Numbers 13:16). The first mention of Joshua as a key figure was in Exodus 17:9 where he was appointed captain of a chosen army to defend Israel against the Amalekites. At the age of forty-four he was called a young man (Exodus 33:11). In whatever circumstances he was found, it seemed his one desire was to know what the will of God was so that he could obey it with all his heart. He was a gifted warrior and statesman who brought honor to God and his nation. His leadership activities were recorded in great detail, but interestingly, no evil attitude or action can be found among them. Joshua was a man whose heart was completely God's.

His leadership activities were recorded in great detail, but interestingly, no evil attitude or action can be found among them. Joshua was a man whose heart was completely God's.

Joshua's Directions for Duty
Joshua 1:1-18 In a most touching way, God announced to Joshua, *"Moses my servant is dead."* God had loved Moses and had faithfully and continually empowered him to serve with courage. The nation had mourned for him thirty days. But now, with much more work ahead, God turned to Joshua, Moses' chief aid for forty years, and said, *"Now therefore, arise, go over this Jordan, you and all this people, to the land which I am giving to them..."* All the years of earlier service

had prepared Joshua for this moment. In the same way, whatever you are called to do now or have done in the past is your preparation for a future service. Don't hesitate to tackle new jobs or learn new skills, whatever your age; they are "deposits" in your talent or experience account to be drawn on as the Lord requires.

All the years of earlier service had prepared Joshua for this moment. In the same way, whatever you are called to do now or have done in the past is your preparation for a future service.

Whose Land Is It? God announced the boundaries of the land He had promised Israel, and He assured Joshua that the nation would have success in possessing it. However, only once in Scripture, in the time of King Solomon, was Israel reported as approaching these extensive boundaries, and even then they were not held for long (1 Kings 4:21,24). Since God assured full and eternal possession, there must still be a time in Israel's future when these boundaries will permanently be hers. God does not give empty promises.

However, even with future success assured, Joshua needed faith and courage in the present to carry out the detailed work of driving out the people who were living in Canaan at that time. Did this sound a bit "ungodly" of God to move one group of people out of the place where they had lived for generations just so another group could move in? The Arab and Palestinian population today in the Middle East often pose this very question. Yet, we must look at the "big picture" to gain understanding and to be satisfied that our God cannot do anything "ungodly."

First, As Creator, God owns everything and can do with it as He wills. He had full authority to promise Israel a specific piece of real estate.

Second, Abraham received this promise of Canaan over four hundred years before. God delayed the actual possession of it until the heathen people who were living there had been given 400 years to hear of His power, repent, and turn to Him as the One True God. Though many had heard and believed the reports of His miracles on behalf of Israel, they had not turned to Him. Thus, the inevitable happened: mercy gave way to judgment, and Israel was God's chosen instrument to carry out that judgment.

Third, God is unlimited in resources, and He certainly would have taken care of their needs for land, too, had the Canaanites turned in faith to Him. There is room in God's "house" for all who want to come.

Recognizing the Work of the Holy Spirit The same Holy Spirit who empowered Joshua is available to empower us. But how does He operate? Let's look at Joshua for our lesson:

forsake - to abandon; to give up entirely

The Holy Spirit's work is continual: *"I will not leave you nor forsake you"* (Joshua 1:5). This promise made to Joshua is God's promise to all believers who move forward in faith because they believe God's Word.

The Holy Spirit's work is mutual: *"Be strong and of good courage"* (Joshua 1:6). We must choose the attitude we will have when faced with God's commands. In fact, attitude is often the only thing we have enough control over to choose! God cooperates with us when we offer our bodies for His service. Paul wrote, *"We have this treasure in earthen vessels, that the excellence of the power may be of God and not of us"* (2 Corinthians 4:7). When we choose to give Him full use of our "vessel," He will fill it with His power. The Holy Spirit is a gentleman: He does not **coerce**, but He does cooperate.

coerce - to compel to action by force or threat

The Holy Spirit's work is conditional: *"This Book of the Law shall not depart from your mouth, but you shall meditate in it day and night, that you may observe to do according to all that is written in it. For then you will make your way prosperous, and then you will have good success"* (Joshua 1:8). The Holy Spirit will not empower us for work that is contrary to the Word of God. If we want to be filled with the power of the Holy Spirit (actually we are commanded to be filled, according to Ephesians 5:18), we must make sure that we are obeying Scripture. We will recognize our agreement with Scripture only if we, like Joshua, take time to read, consider, and observe it continually.

prosperous - marked by success or economic well-being

The Holy Spirit will not empower us for work that is contrary to the Word of God.

The Holy Spirit's work is supernatural: *"Pass through the camp and command the people, saying, 'Prepare provisions for yourselves, for within three days you will cross over this Jordan, to go in to possess the land which the Lord your God is giving you to possess'"* (Joshua 1:11). Crossing the Jordan River at its flood stage with two to three million people would have been impossible for Israel after coming out of forty years of desert life with no boats or lumber to build any. However, what is impossible with man, is very possible with God. The Holy Spirit longs to put the supernatural power of God to work on behalf of man. God's children in every age should expect it.

provisions - a stock of needed materials or supplies

The Holy Spirit's work is adaptable: *"And to the Reubenites, the Gadites, and half the tribe of Manasseh Joshua spoke, saying, ...'Your wives, your little ones, and your livestock shall remain in the land..on this side of the Jordan. But you shall pass before your brethren armed, all your mighty men of valor, and help them'"* (Joshua 1:12,14). Even though these tribes, like many believers today, did not wholly conform to the total plan of God, the Holy Spirit graciously operated in them as much as they would permit Him to do so. Like a home in which certain rooms are kept locked from all visitors, so our lives are often sub-divided into surrendered and unsurrendered areas. When we demand our own way in any particular area of our lives, we are, in essence, refusing entrance to the Holy Spirit there. However, though inhibited, He does not necessarily stop working through the parts of our lives that we have surrendered fully to Him. These 2 1/2 tribes did enjoy military success in the Promised Land, but their choice of residences, which differed from God's plan for them, put them in the unfortunate position of being the first to be **harassed** and conquered by their enemies. The Holy Spirit adapts to our willingness to be used, but how much better for us overall to adapt to His plans without limiting His operation in and through us.

> **harassed** - worried by repeated attack; annoyed continually

Sending of Spies to Jericho
Joshua 2:1-24

Jericho was the most important town in the Jordan Valley. It was the key to Western Canaan, standing at the entrance of the two main passes into the central mountains. Israel would be unable to conquer effectively and unite the whole country if Jericho was allowed to remain a stronghold for enemy operations.

Where Could Strange Men Go Unnoticed?

Jericho was a heathen city. Though perhaps "modern" in architecture, conveniences, and military strength, it was without a devotion to the Lord. Then as now, sexual sin was not uncommon. A house of **prostitution** would attract many customers, and it would actually be a very practical place for spies to go without gathering suspicion about their sudden appearance. The spies may have picked it logically, maybe even attracted by its outside window on the wall, but God had made a divine appointment. Rahab, a prostitute, had heard about His power on behalf of Israel and was willing to give her loyalty to Him. She explained, after recounting the miracles she had heard,"He is God in heaven above and on earth beneath." Rahab's faith had God as its focus. The spies were physically saved because of her help, and she was spiritually saved because of theirs. Others in Jericho had heard the report of God's great power, but she heard, believed, and committed herself to the cause of that God. Because God was and is a God who rewards those who diligently seek Him, no matter from what background they might come, Rahab was not only admitted into the family of Israel, but also honored in Scripture as an ancestor of Jesus. What a lesson this is to us about the love, mercy, and grace of God! No sin can keep us on the outside if we will draw near in faith when we hear the Word declared.

> **prostitution** - the performance of sexual actions in exchange for money or favor

> *Others in Jericho had heard the report of God's great power, but she heard, believed, and committed herself to the cause of that God.*

Blessed for Generations

It is interesting that Scripture recorded that Rahab not only left Jericho to join Israel but also married an Israelite named Salmon. In a later study of the book of Ruth, you will see that Rahab and Salmon were the ancestors of a man named Boaz, a rich landowner, who was extraordinarily kind and generous to a foreign woman named Ruth. With his own relative having been an "outsider" fully accepted in Israel, Boaz obviously had a tender heart for the young Moabite woman, Ruth. When faith blooms in one member of a household, it most often can be seen in future generations, blessing many in its display.

The Scarlet Cord

Every detail of this incident was so meaningful. The red cord used by Rahab to lower the spies down the wall of Jericho for escape was the same one she would tie on the outside of her home as a signal for all gathered there to be spared when Israel came to conquer. The scarlet color reminds us of Christ's blood, because we know that the blood of Jesus saves all who "gather" in faith around its saving power. Rahab was willing to risk her life because of what she believed about God and His people. She was convinced that God could and would clear out the Canaanites and bring Israel into the land, so she risked being caught as a traitor to her own people in order to line up with God's people. Do we believe God and His Word to the extent that we are willing to show that kind of faith-in-action?

Rahab was willing to risk her life because of what she believed about God and His people.

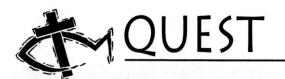QUEST

Questions

Study Procedure: Read the Scripture references before answering questions. Unless otherwise instructed, use the Bible only in answering questions. Some questions may be more difficult than others but try to answer as many as you can. Pray for God's wisdom and understanding as you study and don't be discouraged if some answers are not obvious at first. Do not read the study notes for this lesson until AFTER you have completed your questions.

Day One: Vocabulary Review: Fill in the appropriate word for these definitions.

prosperous   provisions   prostitution   harassed   coerce   forsake

1._____ - a stock of needed materials or supplies

2._____ - the performance of sexual actions for money or favor

3._____ - worried by repeated attack; annoyed continually

4._____ - to abandon; to give up entirely

5._____ - to compel to action by force or threat

6._____ - marked by success or economic well-being

7. What verses in Chapter 2 indicated that others besides Rahab had the information necessary to turn in faith to the God of Israel? _____

Day Two: Read Joshua 3   *MEMORY: ZECHARIAH 7:9-10*

1. The people were to follow _____at a distance as they began their journey into Canaan.

2. What reason was given for this? _____
_____

3. In Joshua 1:11 they had been told to physically prepare themselves for the crossing of the Jordan. Read Joshua 3:5 and write down what else they needed to do. _____
_____

4. For what two purposes was God going to perform visible wonders in front of the people of Israel?
a) verse 7: _____
_____
b) verse 10:_____
_____

Day Three:

1. What was the condition of the Jordan River at this time of year? (See also 1 Chronicles 12:15.)

   _____

2. How would God's choice of this time affect

   a) the miracle itself? _____

   _____

   b) the welfare of His people in the new land? _____

   _____

   _____

3. What would "trigger" the beginning of the miracle? _____

   _____

   _____

Day Four: Read Joshua 4

MEMORY: GENESIS 31:49

1. What job was given to the twelve representatives

   chosen in Joshua 3:12? _____

   _____

   _____

2. What was the purpose of their "memorial"? _____

   _____

   _____

3. Where did Joshua set up his memorial? _____

   _____

   _____

4. Why do you think God so often directed His people to use symbolism, ceremony, or memorial?

   _____

   _____

   _____

5. Do you think these have a place in our lives today? Explain._____

   _____

   _____

   _____

Day Five:

1. The 2 1/2 tribes sent how many men prepared for war to help the other 10 1/2 take the Promised Land? _____

MEMORY: MATTHEW 22:36-39

2. On _____ (the date) at _____ (the place) Israel camped after the miracle at the Jordan River.

3. What was meaningful about that date? _____
   _____

4. As in Deuteronomy, there was an emphasis here on teaching children about God and His Word. What verses mentioned this? _____

5. Do you have any personal thoughts you would like to express about how God reveals Himself in fresh ways to those who want to serve Him? _____
   _____
   _____
   _____

6. Now take a few minutes to read your study notes for this lesson.

Notes

God at Work

Faith Discovered
Review of Joshua 2

Did you notice that Joshua did not send twelve spies into Jericho—just two? He did not want another committee decision but just some basic military intelligence about the enemies they were about to meet. The question of going in was settled; he just wanted to know what to expect once they got in. Joshua probably hand-picked those two men of courage and faith. Yet, the incident of their being seen by someone who reported to the king of Jericho, revealed the faith of another. Rahab, a prostitute or harlot, was probably not surprised to see strangers in her place of business, but when she discovered their true identity, strangely, she did not report them or cooperate with the king's messengers. Instead, she hid them and arranged for their escape. Why? Scripture explained that she had heard, as had her countrymen, all about the power of the God of Israel and believed that He would certainly keep His Word and overtake Jericho for His people, too. Based on what she heard, she made a decision to line up on the side of Israel's God and believed that He would accept her. Rahab's faith could later have been defined by the words of the writer of Hebrews in chapter eleven, verse six: *"But without faith it is impossible to please Him, for he who comes to God must believe that He is, and that He is a rewarder of those who diligently seek Him."* That same writer said of Rahab, *"By faith the harlot Rahab did not perish with those who did not believe, when she had received the spies with peace"* (verse 31). The two spies, obviously aware of the wonderful ways of their God, promised her safety if she would stay where they could find her on their return, in the house marked by the scarlet rope.

Faith Reported

The two spies returned to Joshua with the wonderful report: *"Truly the Lord has delivered all the land into our hands, for indeed all the inhabitants of the country are fainthearted because of us."* The very next day after the return of the spies, Joshua broke camp at Shittim and the people of Israel moved forward. All the tribes who were to receive their portion of land on the west side of Jordan, and forty thousand chosen warriors from Reuben, Gad, and the half tribe of Manasseh, moved out. What a sight this must have been! They were all united with one purpose of heart and mind. According to Numbers 26:7, 18, and 34, there were 70,580 men of war from the tribes of Reuben, Gad, and half of Manasseh, who remained on the east side of Jordan for the protection of that territory.

Deja vu - (French for already seen) In common language, it means "been there, done that"; or the illusion of having previously experienced something actually being encountered for the first time.

Faith Steps Forward
Joshua 3:1-17

Deja vu. Just forty years before, their parents faced a similar crisis: the Red Sea stopped their exit from Egypt. Now, the Jordan River at flood stage blocked Israel's entrance into Canaan. A test of faith and obedience for the young nation, it was, but they trusted God, and God made a way again where there seemed to be no way.

A test of faith and obedience for the young nation, it was, but they trusted God, and God made a way again where there seemed to be no way.

The Ark Takes the Lead

The Lord ordered the ark of the covenant out of its normal, protected place in the center of camp and into the lead position. The Levites were to carry it and set the direction for the march into the new territory, and the general population was to follow at a careful distance of about three-fourths of a mile, so as not to mistake the way.

Wait a Minute!
Joshua 3:5

"Sanctify yourselves, for tomorrow the Lord will do wonders among you." To get the most out of the miracle that was about to occur, Joshua ordered the people to take time

out to examine themselves for any sinful behavior or attitude. Sanctify means to set something apart for a particular use. As Christians we are to give our attention, talent, and treasure only to the things that please God. In everyday living, however, we often get distracted with all sorts of activities and find ourselves offending others with our selfishness or being offended by the selfishness of others. When we are busy "keeping score" with one another, we cannot give our full attention to the things of God. So, Joshua's order to "sanctify yourselves" was appropriate here. They were to stop and get things straight with God and with one another so that they could give their full attention to the miracle that God planned to perform in stopping the flow of the Jordan for them to cross. God sanctifies us with His own Holy Spirit who teaches us and leads us from within, but we have a duty, like Israel did, to confess and correct those things that the Holy Spirit brings to our attention.

As Christians we are to give our attention, talent, and treasure only to the things that please God.

Why a Miracle?
Joshua 3:6-17

Joshua 3:15 and 1 Chronicles 12:15 recorded that at the time of Israel's crossing, near the spring feast of Passover, the Jordan River was at flood stage. The supernatural stopping of the waters was to be a great encouragement to Israel: *"By this you shall know that the living God is among you, and that He will without fail drive out from before you the Canaanites."* Frequently in our lives, as in the history of Israel, we come upon situations that are clearly impossible for us to change by ourselves. However, when we are sure of God's directions for us, and this "impossibility" still blocks our way, we must believe that God intends to remove it. How soon does He work? Well, the priests carrying the ark of the covenant were told to go up to the river and step in: that was the moment God took over. God is never late. His timing is often not in line with what we think it should be, but His timing is perfect. With faith, but without fear, the priests were told to step right up to the challenge that overwhelmed them, and from that point, they had the best view of God at work in their behalf.

However, when we are sure of God's directions for us, and this "impossibility" still blocks our way, we must believe that God intends to remove it.

What It Means

Entering the Promised Land has a parallel in the Christian life. Just as Israel's exodus symbolized the Christian's new birth (a coming out of the kingdom of Satan and into the kingdom of God), so Israel's entrance into Canaan pictured the life of victorious usefulness, that every Christian was created to enjoy with God. It is impossible for us to live up to God's high standard by ourselves; just as it was impossible for Israel to cross the flooded Jordan. Even with our new birth, we must have God's miraculous power through the Holy Spirit, who now lives in us to remove the barrier of "self" that keeps us from listening to and obeying the will of God. The crossing of the Jordan, pictures the death and burial of our own will and the coming out into the Promised Land in the resurrection power of the Holy Spirit.

Every time we want to "take back" control, we must remember that we have died, and our lives are hidden with Christ in God (Colossians 3:3).

The Memorial Stones
Joshua 4:1-24

As humans, we have short memories. At an emotional moment we can be overwhelmed with the greatness of God and can commit ourselves to His service. Then we can get distracted with the duties of daily living and forget our commitment. Joshua had a visual aid, a rocky reminder, built from stones taken out of the Jordan to help Israel remember the day they left the wilderness and entered Canaan. He put one set in the middle of the Jordan, the top of which would show at different seasons, and the other set at their first camping spot at Gilgal, each made with twelve stones representing the twelve tribes of Israel. These stone memorials, through the years, would cause younger people to ask their elders to explain them, and, thus, each generation would be taught and reminded about God's power and Israel's covenant with Him.

What memorial "stones" jog your memory about the goodness of God or your commitment to Him?

Reminders or memorials are still helpful in keeping our minds focused on where we have been and where we are going. What memorial "stones" jog your memory about the goodness of God or your commitment to Him? Make a practice of writing down and dating the significant things that occur between God and you. What has He said in a certain Scripture that made you respond with a new commitment or humbly seek His forgiveness for a repeated sin? Is there a place that is special because of what occurred there or a person who was a witness to an important decision? Allow the Holy Spirit to remind you of things, and don't hesitate to answer the questions asked by others about your personal "memorials."

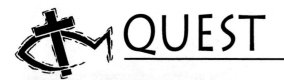

QUEST

Questions

Study Procedure: Read the Scripture references before answering questions. Unless otherwise instructed, use the Bible only in answering questions. Some questions may be more difficult than others but try to answer as many as you can. Pray for God's wisdom and understanding as you study and don't be discouraged if some answers are not obvious at first. Do not read the study notes for this lesson until AFTER you have completed your questions.

MEMORY: COLOSSIANS 3:2-4

Day One: Read Joshua 5:1-12

1. The movement of 2 to 3 million people across a supernaturally stopped river was not something that could be kept secret.

   a) What other groups heard about it? _____

   _____

   _____

   b) With what results? _____

2. It would seem that the perfect time to begin an assault on the Canaanites would have been right after the Jordan miracle, while the enemies were all scared. But this was not what God directed Joshua to do. What was God's first order to Joshua? _____

   _____

3. What was the meaning of this special surgery? (See Genesis 17:1-15.) _____

   _____

4. What verse showed Israel's weakness or vulnerability at this time? _____

5. **Challenge:** Can you think of any other time when God put Israel in a vulnerable position right before He delivered them? _____

   _____

   _____

   _____

Day Two:

MEMORY: ROMANS 1:16

1. What was the meaning of the name "Gilgal"?

   _____

   _____

2. What does the circumcision of Israel and the naming of Gilgal have to teach us as Christians? (See Deuteronomy 10:16; Deuteronomy 30:6; Romans 2:29.) _____

_____

_____

3. What was the first holy festival celebrated in the Promised Land?_____

4. What was new on their daily menu?　_____

Day Three: Joshua 5:13-15

1. What verse showed the boldness or courage of Joshua?　_____

_____

2. What clues are given in this passage as to the real identity of this man Joshua met?

_____

_____

3. Who do you think the Captain was?_____

4. Why do you think Joshua needed this meeting?_____

_____

_____

_____

MEMORY: JOHN 5:24

Day Four: Read Joshua Chapter 6

1. Summarize the battle plan God issued to Joshua for the defeat of Jericho. _____

_____

_____

_____

_____

_____

_____

2. What qualities were needed by the men of war to execute this plan? _____

_____

_____

3. What do you think God was illustrating with this strange strategy? _____

_____

_____

_____

4. What specific instructions did God issue about the execution of those found living in Jericho?

_____

_____

5. What were God's instructions about taking home any "loot" from Jericho? _____

_____

_____

_____

Day Five: Read Deuteronomy 18:9-14 and
Numbers 33:50-56

MEMORY: ROMANS 4:7

1. Why would God not allow Israel to live side by side with the inhabitants of Canaan?

_____

_____

_____

2. Jericho was a stronghold, a double-walled city blocking the way into the heart of Canaan. If it
   had not been destroyed, further progress would have been limited and uncertain. What is the
   Jericho in your Christian walk that has kept you from further progress? _____

_____

_____

_____

_____

3. What can you learn from this lesson that would give you help in pulling down the walls of your
   strongholds? _____

_____

_____

_____

4. What curse was placed on the rebuilding of Jericho? (Read 1 Kings 16:34 for its fulfillment.)

_____

_____

_____

5. Now take a few minutes to read your study notes for this lesson.

Notes

First Things First

Catching Up

Israel had safely crossed the flooded Jordan because of God's miraculous help. They had set up memorials so that each time they returned to the border camp at Gilgal they would be reminded of God's power on their behalf. Chapter 5 recorded that the kings near the Jordan River had heard about the miracle at the Jordan and were overwhelmed with fear of Israel and her God. What a perfect time for Joshua to proceed with his military effort to divide and conquer! But, as all believers soon learn, God's way was not man's way.

As the New Testament verse stated the order, _"Seek first the kingdom of God and His righteousness, and all these things shall be added unto you,"_ so Joshua was directed to clear up a major "kingdom" requirement before he led his troops to war. Once at the beginning of Moses' years as leader of Israel, an angel tried to kill him when he was on his way to Egypt because he had not circumcised one of his sons (Exodus 4:24-26). Similarly, Joshua was told to prepare flint knives and circumcise all males born during the last forty years of the wilderness experience since they had not received this personal sign of covenant relationship with God. There were so many, that the scene of these surgeries was called the "hill of the **foreskins**"! God never changes, and He will interrupt the best of our human plans to make us face the spiritual needs of those around us as well as ourselves. No person could expect to have God's protection and blessing if they were not personally related to Him in covenant. The same is true today. Just because your parents are Christians does not automatically make you one. As someone once said, "God does not have any grandchildren." Then, as now, God required individual commitment to Himself, and everything else could wait until that was accomplished.

foreskins - a fold of skin covering the head of the penis

Just because your parents are Christians does not automatically make you one. As someone once said, "God does not have any grandchildren."

The circumcision procedure caused the men and boys to be very sore for a few days, so they *"stayed in their places in the camp till they were healed"* (Joshua 5:8). They had to rely completely on God for their defense during their recovery, as they were surrounded by enemies, but their trust was well-placed. Their job was to obey, and God promised to provide whatever was needed. God told them, after this requirement was satisfied, that He had *"rolled away the reproach of Egypt"* from them; this tied in well with the name of their camping spot, Gilgal, which meant "rolling" or "wheel." The past was settled, and they were ready to face the future with a clean slate.

Another spiritual matter had to be faced before rushing off to the duties of war. They prepared and celebrated the Passover. The wilderness menu of manna was changed at last to the grain and bread of the land. What a joyful time it must have been! They obediently did the spiritual things first, and, true to His Word, God began to "add all the rest."

| **Special Appearance** | One day when Joshua was near the stronghold of Jericho, perhaps sizing it up for future attack, he saw a striking figure holding a sword in hand. Joshua, never the coward, |

boldly approached the figure asking, *"Are You for us or for our **adversaries**?"* (The New King James version capitalizes the pronouns used here as it does only when referring to God.) Oddly, the Man said, *"No,"* on both accounts. He was not "for" any group, but He was the Commander of the army of the Lord. The point here was that God does not choose a certain group, because He remains constant and stable; a group must choose to follow Him, and then it can expect success. Joshua fell down in an act of worship, and the Man did not protest. In fact, the Man told Joshua to perform another act of worship by removing his shoes. This was a holy place and a holy moment. Joshua had been blessed with an encouraging visit by God in human form, or as we know Him, Jesus. Remember that Jesus is God and has always existed. He came into our earthly history at a certain time and place, but He was present and on duty even at Creation (John 1:1-4). An Old Testament appearance of Jesus was called a theophany, God revealing Himself to man in a form that could be seen without destroying the person looking. How encouraging for Joshua to know that God was so near with spiritual troops on hand to help Israel as they faced the enemies of Canaan! (For another interesting reference to the revealing of spiritual troops on Israel's behalf see 2 Kings 6.)

adversaries - enemies; opponents

Remember that Jesus is God and has always existed. He came into our earthly history at a certain time and place, but He was present and on duty even at Creation.

| **Unusual Military Tactics** **Joshua 6** | Jericho was a double-walled fortress city that blocked Israel from further entrance into Canaan. Archeologists excavated the ruins of Jericho to discover the remains of |

two thirty-foot-high walls, running nearly parallel to each other, made of sun-dried brick. The inside wall was eleven-to-twelve-feet thick and the outer wall was about six-feet thick. Houses, like the kind Rahab would have had, were built spanning both walls. The walls were collapsed outwardly with evidence of a fire throughout the city. The attack must have come suddenly as there were found bins full of grain and ovens with bread still inside. (Information taken from *Thompson Chain Reference Bible,* p. 338.)

Jericho was the site of their first battle to gain control of all of Canaan. Joshua had had military experience already, but he was not the one to plan this battle. God Himself gave some unusual directions for Jericho's capture. When followed, this plan would give total glory to God, but it required the obedience of the entire army of Israel. Once a day for six days, armed Israeli troops led a **procession** around the city of Jericho followed by seven priests blowing ram's horn trumpets, Levites carrying the ark of the covenant, and a rearguard of soldiers. On day seven, they encircled the city seven times, and on that last time, when Joshua gave the command, all the army shouted loudly. With this act of obedience, the walls *"fell down flat"* because God had given them the city.

procession - a group moving forward in an orderly way

What We Can Learn?

Can you imagine what Israel's troops were thinking that week as they marched around like targets, watched suspiciously by the people in Jericho's walled fortress? God could have destroyed Jericho in countless ways, but He chose one that would test the willingness of His people to simply obey what He spoke. They obeyed because they believed that as He had so often done before, God would come through in His time on their behalf. The people in Jericho would also see that Israel's God was fully responsible for their defeat, since His warriors did nothing but shout. We must wonder if Rahab had to bolster the courage and faith of her family as they waited in her home for the seven days, never knowing just when their deliverance would come. The next time God leads you in an unusual manner, maybe nudging you to be silent and walk your faith by example, remember that your complete obedience will keep you out of the way while God works in your behalf. Trust Him to help you tear down strongholds that hold you back. But don't be surprised by the unusually simple things He leads you to do. J.B. Phillips paraphrases 2 Corinthians 10:3-5,6 on this subject this way: *"The truth is that, although of course we lead normal human lives, the battle we are fighting is on the spiritual level. The very weapons we use are not those of human warfare but powerful in God's warfare for the destruction of*

They obeyed because they believed that as He had so often done before, God would come through in His time on their behalf.

Trust Him to help you tear down strongholds that hold you back. But don't be surprised by the unusually simple things He leads you to do.

*the enemy's strongholds. Our battle is to bring down every **deceptive** fantasy and every imposing defense that men erect against the true knowledge of God. We even fight to capture every thought until it acknowledges the authority of Christ."*

deceptive - tricky; untrue

How It Ended	Moses had written in Deuteronomy about the **despicable** practices of those not just in Jericho but in all of Canaan. He

despicable - deserving to be despised

warned Israel ahead of time that they were not to *"learn to follow the abominations of those nations"* (Deuteronomy 18:9). Some of the sins that God used Israel to judge at Jericho were child-sacrifice, witchcraft, soothsaying, worship of the dead, and various occult practices. So, after the walls fell down, the army proceeded to obey God as His instrument of judgment and killed all the inhabitants except those of Rahab's household. They took the silver and gold and bronze and iron vessels to the treasury of the Lord. Joshua pronounced a curse on anyone who attempted to rebuild what God had destroyed. Years later, someone did rebuild Jericho, but at the high cost prophesied by Joshua's curse: the death of his firstborn and youngest child (1 Kings 16:34).

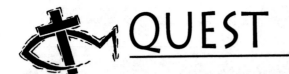

Questions

Study Procedure: Read the Scripture references before answering questions. Unless otherwise instructed, use the Bible only in answering questions. Some questions may be more difficult than others but try to answer as many as you can. Pray for God's wisdom and understanding as you study and don't be discouraged if some answers are not obvious at first. Do not read the study notes for this lesson until AFTER you have completed your questions.

Day One: Vocabulary Multiple Choice: Underline the correct definition for each word:

1. adversaries -

    a) commercials

    b) opponents

    c) teachers

2. deceptive -

    a) tricky; untrue

    b) deep

    c) sad

3. despicable -

    a) mysterious

    b) deserving to be despised

    c) chewable

4. foreskin -

    a) skin on a forehead

    b) a fold of skin covering the head of the penis

    c) new skin growth

5. procession -

    a) a celebration

    b) a meeting where voting occurs

    c) a group moving forward in an orderly way

6. In the preceding notes, Deuteronomy 18 described the sins that brought judgment on Canaan. As you consider child-abuse, abortion, obsession with sex, and increasing involvement with the occult in our own country, do you feel there is reason for concern for the future of our nation, which has had access to the Word of God for so long? _____

    _____

    _____

    _____

Day Two: Read Joshua 6:18 and Chapter 7

MEMORY: 1 Corinthians 16:13

1. One man named_____ from the tribe of _____ took some valuable objects home for his personal use after the battle of Jericho, directly against God's orders. (See Joshua 6:18.)

2. No one else in Israel knew about the secret sin, and so they all assumed that God's power and blessing would follow them in their next battle as it had in Jericho. But they were wrong. What happened? _____

_____

_____

_____

3. What verses record Joshua's shock at Israel's embarrassing defeat at Ai? _____

4. When Joshua prayed for an explanation, God was quick to respond. Summarize what God told Joshua. _____

_____

_____

_____

Day Three:

1. After the Lord singled out Achan from all the rest of Israel, Joshua questioned him about his sin. Summarize Achan's confession. _____

_____

_____

_____

2. Why do you think he was tempted by a beautiful piece of clothing as well as the gold?

_____

_____

_____

_____

3. What tempts you to disobey God? _____

_____

_____

4. List the groups of people affected by Achan's secret sin. _____

_____

_____

Day Four: Read Joshua 8

1. Contrast the second attack on Ai with the

   first one in Chapter 7.

   MEMORY: 2 CORINTHIANS 4:16

	Chapter 7	Chapter 8

   a) size of the army _____

   b) strategy _____

   c) instructions for taking personal "loot" home _____

   _____

   d) final results _____

2. From each verse below, describe what Joshua did before, during, or after this battle:

   a) Joshua 8:1 _____

   b) Joshua 8:3 _____

   c) Joshua 8:9 _____

   d) Joshua 8:10 _____

   _____

   e) Joshua 8:18, 26 _____

   _____

   _____

   f) Joshua 8:28 _____

   g) Joshua 8:30 _____

3. Share with your group any thoughts that you have about Joshua's role here. _____

   _____

   _____

Day Five: Re-read Joshua 8:30-35

MEMORY: 2 CORINTHIANS 12:9-10

1. Moses had given instructions for this

   particular activity before he died. From your column references, write down the Bible reference

   where that occurred. _____

2. Describe the scene at Mt. Ebal and Mt. Gerizim. _____

   _____

   _____

   _____

3. Why do you think Joshua had the people assemble to hear every word Moses had written?

_____

_____

_____

4. What happens when people are exposed to the Word of God? _____

_____

_____

5. Give one or two examples from your own life where Scripture has made a great impact on your actions or attitudes. _____

_____

_____

_____

6. Take a few minutes to read your study notes for this lesson.

Notes

Secret Sin

The High Cost of Sin
Joshua 7

Up to this point in Israel's activities in Canaan, God had miraculously opened up the way: first, through the dividing of the Jordan River so they could come into the area and next through the supernatural collapsing of the double-walls of Jericho so that they could take the city. But just as the manna stopped appearing at their first encampment at Gilgal and they had to depend on the available produce of the land, so after Jericho they were to do more of the fighting themselves as a united army and have less obvious supernatural **intervention**. But of course, without God's blessing, their natural effort would never be enough. They had to remember and follow the first recipe they had been given for success: *"..observe to do according to all the law...do not turn from it to the right hand or to the left, that you may prosper wherever you go"* (Joshua 1:7). Their earthly success depended on their obedience to heaven. With this thought in mind, we will consider the next turn of events.

> **intervention** - coming between to settle a dispute or solve a problem

The Sin

Since Jericho was to have been their very first conquest, God had given orders ahead of the seven-day marching that no one was to take anything for personal use after the victory. As the

As the firstfruits of the season's crops were always offered to God in thanksgiving for His help before the people ate them, so the first spoils of war, the treasures of Jericho, were to be for God's treasury only.

firstfruits of the season's crops were always offered to God in thanksgiving for His help before the people ate them, so the first spoils of war, the treasures of Jericho, were to be for God's treasury only. God intended to allow the soldiers to take their share of **"loot"** or pretty things in future battles, but one man did not wait. Achan, from the tribe of Judah, *"took of the accursed things; so the anger of the Lord burned against the children of Israel"* (Joshua 7:1).

loot - valuable goods taken in war

The Shock

After Jericho, another city stood blocking further penetration of Canaan. It was called Ai and was a city of about 12,000 people, located twelve miles northwest of Jericho. Ai had a more famous neighboring city that would fall if it fell; it was called Bethel. It had been an important site for the early patriarchs, Abraham, Isaac, and Jacob several hundred years before when the land was first promised to them. Since Ai seemed a weakly defended city, the spies suggested that Joshua send only a small army to attack them. Joshua agreed and sent 3,000, but they were somehow overcome with fear when the men of Ai defended the city. To Joshua's horror, they turned and ran in retreat, leaving thirty-six fellow soldiers dead. This disaster made the *"hearts of the people"* melt and become *"like water"* (verse 5).

The Sinner

Joshua was completely taken by surprise by this defeat and tore his clothes in the Hebrew sign of deep grief. He fell on his face to ask the Lord why it all happened. God told him to get up and face the obvious: clearly someone had sinned and caused this catastrophe to fall on the whole nation. Israel was seen as one whole unit, with a violation of God's Word by one being seen as the sin of all. With an interesting parade of tribes, God directed the **elimination** of the innocent and the revelation of the guilty. Achan was singled out. He admitted his sin when confronted and said he had coveted the garment and precious metals, took them for himself, and had them hidden in his tent. He should have known that he could never hide them from God. No one sins in secret, and no one sins without affecting others: thirty-six families mourned the deaths of their loved ones; Joshua was overwhelmed with discouragement at the army's tragic failure; and Achan's own family was sentenced to share in his awful punishment.

elimination - getting rid of

Achan saw the beautiful things, longed for them, and took them. Israel had been at least forty years without stylish clothes or money of their own. The sin was not in noticing what was right in front of him but in dwelling on it, allowing his mind to imagine what he could do with it, when he clearly knew that it was forbidden. *"But each one is tempted when he is drawn away by his own desires and enticed. Then, when desire has conceived, it gives birth to sin; and sin, when it is full-grown, brings forth death"* (James 1:14,15). This was certainly the case with

Achan as it had been with the first man and woman Adam and Eve. James further advised, *"Be doers of the word, and not hearers only, deceiving yourselves"* (James 1:22). Knowing God's word and not obeying it can still be as dangerous for us as it was for Achan.

Knowing God's word and not obeying it can still be as dangerous for us as it was for Achan.

The Sentence

Achan and his family were executed by stoning and then burned along with all their possessions. His sin had severely troubled Israel and the heap or mound marking his execution was called the Valley of Achor or Valley of Trouble. How high a price was required for Achan's sin! That same cost is still required of us for our sins, but Jesus made Himself available to pay it in our place. If we will accept His offer, our Valley of Achor can be turned, as recorded in Hosea 2:15, into a *"door of hope."* Israel would leave that scene humbled and more determined to obey God's every command.

"If at first you don't succeed..." Joshua 8

Joshua heard God's command to get up and go and try again to defeat Ai. However, this time God gave the battle strategy. Joshua picked 30,000 soldiers to do the job. He sent them away at night to take a position behind the city of Ai. In the daylight, Joshua positioned a 5,000-man force to the west of the city. He led the rest of Israel to a position in front of the city, which was to the north. The people of Ai saw Joshua's group across the valley and assumed that if they attacked Israel, Israel would again run away. However, when the men of Ai and the neighboring city Bethel pursued Israel and Israel did start **retreating**, the hidden army of 30,000 came from behind the city and burned it. The men of Ai looked back, saw it burning, but now were caught between Joshua and his troops, the eastern army of 5,000 and the 30,000 in front of their city. The ambush plan worked, and Israel killed 12,000 that day, taking livestock and spoil back to their families. Joshua took a position much like Moses had in an earlier war with the Amalekites, that of **intercessor**. As God instructed, he held out his spear, visually demonstrating the direction to which he wanted God's power to be active, until the victory was complete.

retreating - withdrawing; going away from

intercessor - one who offers prayer or petition in favor of another

Remembering to say "Thank You!" Joshua 8:30-35

Back in Deuteronomy 27 and 28, Moses had left orders for Joshua to lead Israel in a special assembly so they could hear again the complete law of God. Like a natural **amphitheater** or outdoor auditorium, the two mountains of Gerizim and Ebal provided a perfect scene for carrying out this order. Joshua put six tribes on one mountain and six on the other, with the ark of the covenant stationed between them. Joshua built an altar of whole stones, as Moses had required. No tool was used on them

amphitheater - a flat or gently sloping area surrounded by abrupt slopes

Reading God's Word and thanking Him with worship should be scheduled into each day in the life of a Christian.

since God did not want any carved images to interfere with the true worship He required. Joshua re-wrote the law on stones and then afterward read it all to the assembled people. How appropriate after victory to worship the one who made it possible and to review His will so that He could be obeyed in everything. Reading God's Word and thanking Him with worship should be scheduled into each day in the life of a Christian. Someone wrote that delayed gratitude is ingratitude, and ingratitude is like stealing. Are we robbing God of what belongs to Him in the area of worship and study? Only you can evaluate your own dedication to Him.

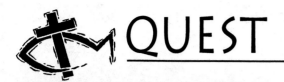 **QUEST**

Questions

Study Procedure: Read the Scripture references before answering questions. Unless otherwise instructed, use the Bible only in answering questions. Some questions may be more difficult than others but try to answer as many as you can. Pray for God's wisdom and understanding as you study and don't be discouraged if some answers are not obvious at first. Do not read the study notes for this lesson until AFTER you have completed your questions.

Day One: Vocabulary Matching

MEMORY: GALATIANS 2:20

_____1. loot	a)	a flat or gently sloping area surrounded by abrupt slopes
_____2. elimination	b)	getting rid of
_____3. retreating	c)	one who offers prayer or petition in favor of another
_____4. amphitheater	d)	coming between to settle a dispute or solve a problem
_____5. intervention	e)	valuable goods taken in war
_____6. intercessor	f)	withdrawing; going away from

7. What have you learned this year about the importance of obedience to God's Word?

_____

_____

_____

Day Two: Read Joshua 9

MAP STUDY

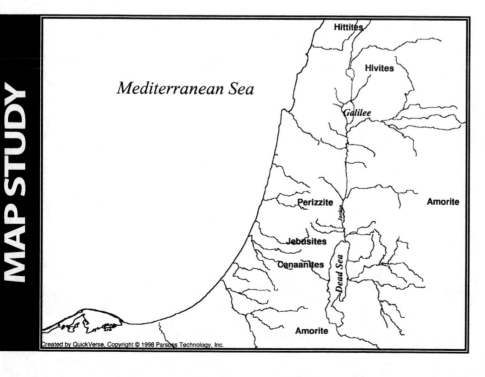

1. Locate on your map of Canaan the six enemy tribes listed here: Hittite, Amorite, Canaanite, Perizzite, Hivite, and Jebusite.

2. To which Canaanite tribe did Gibeon belong?_____

3. The Gibeonites had heard of God's power on behalf of Israel and had adopted the philosophy,
    "If you can't beat them, join them."

    a) How did they convince Israel that they were from a distant place?   _____

    _____

    _____

    b) What did they want from Israel?   _____

4. What verses revealed the leaders' uncertainty about them? _____

5. Read the following passages: Exodus 23:31,32: *"And I will set your bounds....For I will deliver the
    inhabitants of the land into your hand, and you shall drive them out before you. You shall make no
    covenant with them,nor with their gods."* Numbers 33:55: *"But if you do not drive out the inhabitants
    of the land from before you, then it shall be that those whom you let remain shall be irritants in your
    eyes and thorns in your sides, and they shall harass you in the land where you dwell."* Deuteronomy
    7:2: *"And when the Lord your God delivers them over to you, you shall conquer them and utterly
    destroy them. You shall make no covenant with them nor show mercy to them."* Now, answer this:
    Do you think Israel would have made covenant with the Gibeonites if they had known their true
    identity? _____

Day Three: Continue reading Joshua 9   **MEMORY: GALATIANS 6:7,9-10**

1. What did the elders neglect to do in their
    handling of this situation?_____

    _____

2. What was the result? _____

    _____

3. How did Israel find out they had been tricked? _____

    _____

    _____

4. A covenant was binding as long as both parties lived. Israel could not break the covenant, so
    what did they do? _____

    _____

Day Four: Read Joshua 10

1. A covenant relationship brings responsibilities to both partners. One is mutual protection. When Israel was willing to keep covenant and help Gibeon, God turned the obligation into a blessing. Explain: _____

 MEMORY: EPHESIANS 6:10-12

_____

_____

2. What two miracles did God perform to help Israel gain complete victory?

_____

_____

3. Read Joshua 10:21. What interesting details are given here about Israel's victory?

_____

4. In Joshua 10:28-43 Israel headed south and conquered seven more cities. Give the verses recording the defeat of each of these cities:

   a) Makkedah _____

   b) Libnah _____

   c) Lachish_____

   d) Gezer _____

   e) Eglon _____

   f) Hebron_____

   g) Debir _____

5. From the last verses of chapter ten, give the reasons for Israel's successes.

_____

_____

Day Five: Read Joshua 11

1. Now Joshua headed his army northward. Many kings had joined together to fight Israel and they had a military advantage. What was it? _____

_____

_____

2. What word of encouragement did God give Joshua about this? _____

_____

_____

3. What was the final outcome? _____

_____

_____

4. Read Joshua 12. This is a roll call of the defeated enemies of Israel.

   a) Which verses list the battles won under Moses? _____

   b) Which verses list the battles won under Joshua? _____

5. Now take a few minutes to read your study notes for this lesson.

Notes

Friends and Enemies

Israel's Good News Traveled Fast! Joshua 9

After Israel conquered Jericho and then succeeded at Ai and Bethel, she gained a reputation among the remaining cities of Canaan as an awesome enemy. So, in self-defense, groups of cities banded together to face Israel. However, one city called Gibeon, near the present camp of Israel, decided not to fight Israel but to join them. This joining together with another person or group was called making covenant, and as we have studied earlier in this series, it had mutual requirements and life-long benefits once it was agreed upon and sealed. God had warned Israel to make no covenants with the inhabitants of Canaan, because after centuries of wickedness, He was bringing His judgment on them, intending to use Israel to carry it out. Being bound to people who did not recognize the true God would only bring problems and temptations to Israel.

This joining together with another person or group was called making covenant, and as we have studied earlier in this series, it had mutual requirements and life-long benefits once it was agreed upon and sealed.

Can't Beat 'em? Join 'em! Joshua 9

Even though the city of Gibeon was bigger than the recently defeated Ai and Bethel, it still did not want to face Israel in battle. Using trickery and deceit, they convinced Israel that they were from far away and wanted to make a covenant of friendship so that Israel would not attack them. Cleverly they mentioned distant miracles, not the recent ones God had brought about, wore old clothes, and brought old bread and wine. *"Then the men of Israel took some of their provisions;"* (part of making a covenant was to share food) *"but they did not ask counsel of the Lord"* (Joshua 9:14). Big mistake! What trouble we could save ourselves if we would stop and ask God about our decisions! *"If any of you lacks wisdom, let him ask of God, who gives to all liberally and without reproach"* (James 1:5). Perhaps God would have revealed the

Gibeonites' true identity and then had Israel show mercy anyway, as had happened in the case of Rahab at Jericho. However, when someone has been deliberately tricked or deceived into providing help, there is not the same joy or satisfaction as when that help has been provided freely. The fellowship suffers where truth has been deliberately withheld. No one likes to feel "used."

| **Truth Revealed** | It took only three days for the truth to come out about Gibeon's nearby location. Israel checked it out and found them to be only three days away. To Israel's credit, they did |

not break covenant and attack Gibeon, even though the whole congregation complained about such deception. However, they did decide to get some usefulness from the forced covenant, requiring Gibeon to serve them as woodcutters and water-carriers for the people and for the *"altar of the Lord"* (Joshua 9:27).

| **Covenant Consequences** Joshua 10 | The news of Israel's covenant with Gibeon traveled southwest to the five kings of the Amorites: Adoni-zedek of Jerusalem, Hoham of Hebron, Piram of Jarmuth, Japhia of Lachish, and Debir of Eglon. These kings were alarmed |

because Gibeon was a great city with a reputation for mighty warriors. They decided to unite and go up against Gibeon before it could unite with Israel. Gibeon was able to get word to Israel of the attack and asked them to honor the covenant by coming to help. Israel did the honorable thing and went. Joshua had received encouragement from God about the venture: *"Do not fear them, for I have delivered them into your hand; not a man of them shall stand before you"* (Joshua 10:8). God intended to use this forced covenant relationship to speed up Israel's conquest of Canaan. He would help them overcome this union of the Amorite kings.

| **God's Power Displayed** | Joshua marched his army all night to reach Gibeon, which was about twenty-five miles from their camp at Gilgal, and came upon the enemy troops *"suddenly"* (verse 9). |

The Lord chased them before Israel and *"killed them with a great slaughter"* (verse 10). The Lord sent hailstones on the Amorites, killing more with hail than Israel did with the sword. Joshua, ever the bold warrior, wanted to complete the victory but knew the daylight was running out. With great faith, he called for the sun to stand still until Israel could have *"revenge upon their enemies."* Talk about a miracle! Scientists discuss, astronomers calculate, but man can only imagine the awesome power of our Creator God, who can accomplish the humanly impossible for His children. Verse 14 sums it up: *"And there has been no day like that, before it or after it, that the Lord heeded the voice of a man; for the Lord fought for Israel."*

Talk about a miracle! Scientists discuss, astronomers calculate, but man can only imagine the awesome power of our Creator God, who can accomplish the humanly impossible for His children.

"And there has been no day like that, before it or after it, that the Lord heeded the voice of a man; for the Lord fought for Israel."

Leaders Executed

Israel returned to Gilgal after that great battle, but soon received word that the five kings of the enemy armies were hidden in a cave at Makkedah. Joshua sent word to seal the cave till the fleeing armies were fully conquered as they headed for safety inside their fortified cities. The miraculous works of God had shut the mouths of everyone around (verse 21), and Joshua proceeded to execute the five kings as a **solemn** demonstration of what God intended to do to all the enemies of Israel.

solemn - highly serious

Southern Canaan Now Conquered

Joshua reassembled his troops and went from city to city to finish the conquests: *"So Joshua conquered all the land: the mountain country and the South and the lowland and the wilderness slopes, and all their kings; he left none remaining, but utterly destroyed all that breathed, as the Lord God of Israel had commanded....All these kings and their land Joshua took at one time, because the Lord God of Israel fought for Israel"* (Joshua 10:40-42).

Now for the North
Joshua 11

With the southern region now cleared of the major enemy strongholds and convinced of the power of Israel's God, the north united to face Israel. The kings involved here were Jabin of Hazor, Jobab of Madon, and the kings of Shimron and Achshaph as well as others from the mountains and lowlands inhabited by the Amorites, Hittites, Perizzites, Jebusites, and Hivites. A military advantage this group had, besides their huge numbers, lay in their horses and chariots. Again the Lord was directing Israel, and He encouraged Joshua, *"Do not be afraid because of them, for tomorrow about this time I will deliver all of them slain before Israel. You shall **hamstring** their horses and burn their chariots with fire."*

hamstring - to cripple by cutting the leg tendon

God Keeps His Word

As was his custom, Joshua lost no time in following God's directions and came against them *"suddenly by the waters of Merom"* (Joshua 11:7). The Lord delivered the enemy to Israel and Israel followed through. The horses and chariots that looked so dangerous were now Israel's to disable and destroy. Hamstringing the horses meant cutting a tendon in the back of their legs so that they could not be used for riding or pulling again. Although war is always horrible, there is a lesson for us here. When we obey God's direction for us, He is able to show us how to destroy the weapons that Satan uses against us. Satan brings fear, but we destroy it through hearing and studying the Word of God, which builds up our faith. Satan brings confusion, but we remove it by asking God in prayer for wisdom and direction. Satan brings discouragement, but we free ourselves by confessing our sins to God, receiving His forgiveness, and offering ourselves for the next assignment. There is no weapon formed against us that will prosper when we are empty of self and filled with the Holy Spirit of God.

When we obey God's direction for us, He is able to show us how to destroy the weapons that Satan uses against us.

**Conquests
Counted
Joshua 12**

Joshua 12 recorded the battle history of Israel. Under Moses, Israel had begun its conquests on the eastern side of the Jordan. The Amorite kings Sihon and Og were defeated, and their lands were given to Reuben, Gad, and half of Manasseh. Under Joshua the land west of the Jordan was conquered. The victories over all the "ites" were listed for a total of thirty-one specific conquests.

**What's
Next?**

Joshua had successfully swept the land of Canaan with his united army, cleaning out the major strongholds of enemy power. Now it was time for the twelve tribes and their individual family groups to receive their specific portions of land and to clear out all remaining enemies. Their success was guaranteed if they would go forward immediately as Joshua had, depending on the Lord, being strong and courageous.

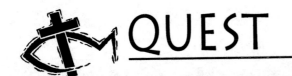

QUEST

Questions

Study Procedure: Read the Scripture references before answering questions. Unless otherwise instructed, use the Bible only in answering questions. Some questions may be more difficult than others but try to answer as many as you can. Pray for God's wisdom and understanding as you study and don't be discouraged if some answers are not obvious at first. Do not read the study notes for this lesson until AFTER you have completed your questions.

Day One: Vocabulary: Fill in the blanks with the appropriate vocabulary word from your notes.

1. Covenant making is a _____ act because it is in effect as long as you live.

2 When Joshua wanted to make sure that the enemies' horses would not be used against Israel any more, he ordered his men to _____ them.

3. Describe the two miracles God used to help Israel in their battles. _____

_____

_____

_____

4. Did the episode about the Gibeonites tricking Israel into making a covenant with them teach you something you could record here? _____

_____

_____

_____

Day Two: Read Joshua 13

MEMORY: PHILIPPIANS 4:4-8

1. Describe Joshua's physical condition at this time. _____

_____

2. What else did God want him to do? _____

_____

3. Which verse in this chapter gives us the first hint that Israel was not completely obeying God now? _____

4. The tribe of _____ received no inheritance of land; however they did receive

_____

5. Joshua 13:15-33 described the land given on the _____ side of the Jordan River to _____, _____, and half of _____.

Day Three: Read Joshua 14

MEMORY: 1 JOHN 5

1. From the first verses of Chapter 14, how and by whom was the distribution of the land to the other 9 1/2 tribes carried out? _____

_____

_____

2. Chapter 14:6-15 describes a specific request for land by Caleb.

a) Who was he? _____

_____

b) How was he connected to Joshua? _____

_____

_____

_____

c) How old was he at this time? _____

d) What land did he want? _____

_____

e) Why did he select that particular area? _____

_____

f) What did he think he could do with it? _____

_____

g) How did Caleb *"wholly follow the Lord"*? _____

_____

Day Four: Read Joshua 15

MEMORY: 2 THESSALONIANS 3:3

1. Find a map with the allotments of the different tribes pictured. Locate Judah.

2. In Joshua 15:13-19 we read more about Caleb. The children of Anak were giants. How many did he drive off his land? _____

3. In asking for help to finish the work, Caleb also was making sure that his future son-in-law would be a man of courage. Who took the challenge? _____

_____

4. What do you learn here about the relationship of Caleb and his daughter? _____

_____

_____

_____

5. If Achsah's actions were used as an example of what prayer to our Heavenly Father should be like, what would they illustrate? _____

_____

_____

Day Five: Read Joshua 16-21

Fill in the blanks from the list of answers provided. Some may be used **more than once.**

Joshua, Zelophehad, Shiloh, Issachar, Asher, Benjamin, **Simeon,** Ephraim, Manasseh, cities of refuge, Dan, Naphtali, Zebulun

1. In Joshua 16, the tribes of Joseph's sons _____ and _____ received their land.

2. In Joshua 17, the daughters of _____ inherited land even though they had no men left to inherit (verses 3-6).

3. In Joshua 17:14-18, _____ and _____ complained that

_____

they needed more land. _____ told them to clear out the enemies in the land they had already been given and they could have some more.

4. In Chapter 18, Israel camped at _____ and set up the tabernacle there.

5. In Chapter 18:4-10, Joshua sent out representatives to go out and draw boundaries for the remaining seven sections of land, evidently to make sure that they were all about equal in size and resources. Then he would draw lots to see which tribe got which section. List (from Joshua 18 and 19) the seven remaining tribes that would get land: _____

_____

_____

6. Chapter 20 describes the location and purpose of the _____.

7. Now take a few minutes to study your notes for this lesson.

Notes

Get On With It!

A Little About the Land

Canaan, also known as the Promised Land, and later Palestine or the Holy Land, is a region to the east of the Mediterranean Sea. Three continents can be reached from its **strategic** location: Europe, Asia, and Africa. Due to its central situation, Canaan became a hub of political, commercial, and religious activity. The land had mountains and plains, rocky hills, and fertile valleys. It was home to a variety of people. The people called Canaanites lived in the cities of the plains. The Amorites lived in the highlands. Other groups mentioned had descriptive names: Perizzite meant peasant; Hivite meant villager; the Horites were cave-dwellers; and the Rephaim, Zazim, Emim, and Anakim were giants.

> **strategic** - of great importance to a particular plan

A Little More About the Leader
Joshua 13

God recognized that Joshua *"was old, advanced in years,"* but He did not excuse him from duty or settle him into retirement because there remained *"very much land yet to be possessed."* Joshua was to move from being a soldier to a statesman. He was to see that each tribe settled into their inheritance and continued the work of driving out the enemies still remaining.

God is aware of everything about us. As our physical bodies change, He often adjusts our duties. No matter what shape we are in, we can expect God to find a task suitable for our abilities. Age affects different people in different ways as we saw in Chapter 14 with Caleb, probably a **contemporary** of Joshua's. Just ask God about His plans for you—do not worry about how He may or may not be using someone else.

> **contemporary** - one of the same age or living at the same time as another

Signs of Compromise

Several times in these chapters a statement **recurred,** recording the fact that Israel did not follow through with what they had started in Canaan. Joshua 13:13 reported one of these failures to obey: *"Nevertheless the children of Israel did not drive out the Geshurites or the Maachathites, but the Geshurites and the Maachathites dwell among the Israelites until this day."* We, like Israel, will fail to receive the full blessings God planned for us if we stop short of fulfilling His complete will. Compromise with the enemy brought needless pain and failure.

> **recurred** - occurred again after an interval

> *Compromise with the enemy brought needless pain and failure.*

Past Land Allotments Reviewed

Moses had already assigned Reuben, Gad, and half of Manasseh the land they requested east of the Jordan River, right outside Canaan. The last half of Chapter 13 reviewed their boundaries.

9 1/2 to Go!
Joshua 14

The "committee" in charge of assigning land to the remaining tribes was made up of Eleazar the High Priest, Joshua, and the heads of the fathers of the tribes of Israel. They used lots to determine who received which portion of land. The 9 1/2 remaining tribes were Judah, Ephraim and Manasseh (Joseph's sons who inherited equal shares with their uncles in place of Joseph's one), Benjamin, Simeon, Zebulun, Issachar, Asher, Naphtali, and Dan. Levi was the priestly tribe and received cities scattered about the country, on both sides of the Jordan, instead of one specific allotment of land.

Who's First?
Joshua 14

Evidently the tribe of Judah was first to receive land. Chapter 14 gave an incident about Caleb, the spy, who with Joshua forty-five years before, gave the minority report about the land of Canaan. He and Joshua wanted to obey God, go right in, and take the land. They were out-voted, but God noted their hearts which *"wholly followed"* God, no matter what everyone else did. He let them live through the deaths of all their contemporaries to be the only two to enter the Promised Land. At 85, this elder of Judah was still full of courage and faith and asked Joshua to make good the earlier promise of Moses to give him the very land he had walked over as a spy. Caleb requested a mountain, inhabited by giants, and Joshua granted his old friend's request.

> *He and Joshua wanted to obey God, go right in, and take the land. They were out-voted, but God noted their hearts which "wholly followed" God, no matter what everyone else did. He let them live through the deaths of all their contemporaries to be the only two to enter the Promised Land.*

Who Will Help?
Joshua 15

Chapter 15 details the boundaries of the land given to Judah, Israel's largest tribe. In between the geography of this chapter and the listing of the major cities was sandwiched another episode related to the courageous Caleb. He had rid his land of three **notorious** giants but still faced more enemies. He had an unmarried daughter named Achsah, for whom he evidently wanted a worthy husband. Caleb issued a challenge. Whoever took the stronghold of Kirjath Sepher could marry his daughter. It would be a great honor for any kinsman of Judah to have the brave Caleb for a father-in-law. Othniel, who later became the first judge of Israel, took the challenge, succeeded, and married Achsah. As bold as her father, she asked for upper and lower springs of water for the land they had conquered. Caleb granted her request for the blessing of water, and we, of course, hope they all lived happily ever after, without any more giants! As far as father-child relationships go, this one appeared very solid and reminds us of how openly we can go to our Heavenly Father to ask for what we need, fully expecting Him to help us.

notorious - widely and unfavorably known

Next!
Joshua 16 and 17

The two sons of Joseph had tribes named Ephraim and Manasseh, and they inherited full shares with their uncles' tribes in Joseph's place. Manasseh had already received half its portion east of the Jordan but here received the rest, along with Ephraim. The earlier appeal of the daughters of Zelophehad, who wanted to inherit land even though they had no males to receive it for them, was settled in Chapter 17 when they received their portion. According to Joshua 16:10, Ephraim failed to clear out all the enemy peoples from its land and yet in Joshua 17:14 complained with Manasseh that it needed more land for its large population. Joshua told them to go clear some more out if they needed it, but Ephraim and Manasseh wanted some land without enemies who drove iron chariots. Joshua, in essence, told them to take his offer because they were able to win even over chariots of iron.

How often are we not satisfied with our "lot" in life? We do not want to work harder at getting victory where we are but would rather start all over in some other area. We appeal to God as if He had made some mistake in putting us where we are, but He, like Joshua, most often makes us face up to the challenges in our own backyard before promising us any relief or new location. Ephraim and Manasseh lacked the courageous whole-heartedness of Caleb and Joshua, and their tribes would suffer. Are we causing others to suffer because we won't face up to our current responsibilities? We need to confess our fears and ask God to give us His power to face what is before us.

> *We appeal to God as if He had made some mistake in putting us where we are, but He, like Joshua, most often makes us face up to the challenges in our own backyard before promising us any relief or new location.*

New Home for the Tabernacle; No Homes for the Seven
Joshua 18

All Israel came together for the reassembling of the tabernacle at Shiloh. They had enjoyed many victories as a united nation, but seven individual tribes had still not received their land. Joshua asked them how long they would *"neglect to go and possess the land which the Lord God of your fathers has given you?"* (Joshua 18:3). Like the landless seven, we sometimes watch others jump right in to receive what they have heard or read from Scripture that God has promised—perhaps promises of help or wisdom or supply or patience or success. However, we hang back, almost afraid to take the first step to obey because of what it might cost us. We forget that what God has planned for us is a *"future and a hope"* (Jeremiah 29:11), and is well worth any sacrifice or struggle to possess it. What are you waiting for?

How to Get a Fair Share

Joshua issued some directions for dividing the land that would be great today for people having to divide anything into **equivalent** shares. (Athletic teams especially come to mind!) He had them select for themselves three representatives from each of their seven tribes to report to him. He sent these out to survey the remaining land and to draw up and agree upon boundaries that would make each of the

equivalent - equal in force, amount, or value

seven "lots" equivalent in size and value. They would not all be alike, but where one had an advantage of one kind, another would be drawn to include some other valuable resource to balance it. Then, when they all agreed that the seven lots were equivalent, Joshua would cast lots to decide which tribe got which lot. In this way Benjamin, Simeon, Zebulun, Issachar, Asher, Naphtali, and Dan received their lands.

The Accuracy of Scripture

Even though the boundary lines were drawn up by a select committee and assigned by casting lots, the Scriptural prophecies about each of these tribes given by Jacob (450 years before) and Moses (about 7 years before) were fulfilled. Read the following examples:

Reuben, *"unstable as water, you shall not excel"* (Genesis 49:4). Reuben received land on the east side of Jordan and would be among the first to be captured and carried away by enemies in later years. No important leaders, prophets, or judges ever came from this tribe.

Simeon and Levi, *"...I will divide them in Jacob and scatter them in Israel"* (Genesis 49:7b). Simeon and Levi did not receive separate portions of land as did the other tribes. Simeon had its land given within the borders of Judah (Joshua 19:1), and Levi had cities and surrounding common lands given to it from each of the other tribes scattered on both sides of the Jordan (Joshua 21).

Judah, *"you are he whom your brothers shall praise; your hand shall be on the neck of your enemies"* (Genesis 49:8). Judah, the largest tribe, received the largest portion of land and was the tribe from which Jesus came. Jesus is worthy of all praise and has conquered all our enemies. Judah was the only tribe to survive and return as a recognizable unit after the Babylonian captivity.

Zebulun, *"...shall become a haven for ships"* (Genesis 49:13). The lot of Zebulun lay between the Sea of Galilee and the Mediterranean Sea! (Joshua 19).

Issachar, *"a strong donkey lying down between two burdens"* (Genesis 49:14). The word "burdens" can also mean "saddlebags." The donkey was a valuable beast of service, hard-working and dependable. The lot given to Issachar included part of the Jezreel Valley, a scene of many military battles. Issachar's boundary on the north was Mount Tabor and on the south was Mount Gilboa. So, like large burdens, these two mountains were on the sides of Issachar.

Asher, *"Bread from Asher shall be rich, and he shall yield royal dainties"* (Genesis 49:20). Also, *"and let him dip his foot in oil"* (Deuteronomy 33:24c). The word "fat" is the general word used for olive oil. The land Asher received was known for its immense olive groves. Even today, most of the olive oil production comes from Asher's territory. Also, centuries later, an underground oil pipeline would be located underneath it, connecting Mesopotamia to the Mediterranean Sea.

Benjamin, *"the beloved of the Lord shall dwell in safety by Him, who shelters him all the daylong; and he shall dwell between His shoulders"* (Deuteronomy 33:12). Benjamin's lot was like a **buffer** between the two strong tribes of Ephraim and Judah. Its northern border touched Ephraim and its southern boundary topped Judah. It had many important cities in its allotment, the most important being Jerusalem (Joshua 18:28). Jerusalem was home to God's sanctuary or temple and fulfilled Moses' prophecy about the beloved dwelling *"between His shoulders."* Jerusalem was centered in the middle of Benjamin's lot.

> **buffer** - a shield or cushion separating two things

These fulfillments of prophecy are so interesting in light of the fact that Joshua and his "committee" drew up the lines as they thought appropriate and then cast lots to assign them to different tribes. Still, God's plan came about anyway. The truth of Proverbs 16:33 is seen in this: *"The lot is cast into the lap, but its every decision is from the Lord."* God's prophecies always come true in due time.

> *The truth of Proverbs 16:33 is seen in this: "The lot is cast into the lap, but its every decision is from the Lord." God's prophecies always come true in due time.*

Final Assignments
Joshua 20 and 21

The cities of refuge and the cities belonging to the Levites were described and listed in these chapters to complete the division of Canaan. It is interesting to note that God in His **impartiality** was as concerned with providing a place of protection and supply for accused manslayers as He was for His faithful servants the Levites. On whichever side of His will you find yourself, He is the only One who can provide the significance and security for which we all long. As there was a place for every tribe, God has a place for you. Are you still hesitant about stepping forward to possess it? Be strong and of good courage. God is near to help you.

> **impartiality** - fairness

> *As there was a place for every tribe, God has a place for you.*

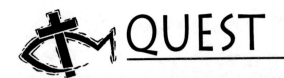 QUEST

Questions

Study Procedure: Read the Scripture references before answering questions. Unless otherwise instructed, use the Bible only in answering questions. Some questions may be more difficult than others but try to answer as many as you can. Pray for God's wisdom and understanding as you study and don't be discouraged if some answers are not obvious at first. Do not read the study notes for this lesson until AFTER you have completed your questions.

MEMORY: JOSHUA 21:45

Day One: Vocabulary Matching

a) buffer
b) contemporary
c) equivalent
d) impartiality
e) notorious
f) recurred
g) strategic

_____1. of great importance to a particular plan

_____2. one of the same age or living at the same time as another

_____3. occurred again after an interval

_____4. widely and unfavorably known

_____5. equal in force, amount, or value

_____6. a shield or cushion separating two things

_____7. fairness

Matching Review:

Ephraim   Gad   Judah   Levi

Manasseh   Simeon   Reuben

8. _____ received the largest portion of land.

9. _____ and _____ had land within other tribes' lands.

10. _____, _____, and the 1/2 tribe of _____

had land east of the Jordan.

11. _____ and _____ wanted more before they had cleared out

what they had.

12. From the end of Joshua 21, copy the verses that summarize the way God kept His promises to

Israel. _____

_____

_____

_____

_____

_____

_____

_____

Day Two: Read Joshua 22

1. Now that the assignment of land had been completed, what did Joshua do in Joshua 22:1-9?

_____

_____

_____

_____

2. Which verse in this section is a warning to the 2 1/2 tribes as they face separation from the others? _____

3. Give an example of a time when you have been separated from your Christian "brothers and sisters" by choice or circumstance and what resulted from it. _____

_____

_____

_____

Day Three: Joshua 22, continued

MEMORY: JOSHUA 22:5

1. According to verse 10, what did Reuben, Gad, and Manasseh build? _____

2. The tribes west of the Jordan were outraged and gathered at _____ to prepare for _____.

3. Fortunately, they asked some questions first.
   a) Whom did they send?_____
   b) He was a good choice because....(find out what he had done before this, looking up his name in a concordance or a column reference) _____

   _____

   _____

   _____

4. Phinehas reminded the 2 1/2 tribes of two incidences in the past that brought judgment on all of Israel.
   a) What were they? _____

   _____

   b) What solution did he offer? _____

   _____

c) How did the 2 1/2 tribes explain their actions?_____
_____
_____
_____

d) How did the western tribes respond to the explanation? _____
_____

5. What lessons can we learn from this in our own lives? _____
_____
_____
_____

Day Four: Read Joshua 23. Realizing his death was near, Joshua gave some final advice to Israel's elders. Give the reference(s) that would correspond to these statements.

1. "I don't have much time left." _____

2. "The Lord has done great things for you." _____

3. "The Lord will do great things for you." _____

4. "You must be careful to obey all He says." _____

5. "There will be great trouble for you if you don't." _____

Day Five: Read Joshua 24

MEMORY: JOSHUA 24:15

1. Joshua continued to lead Israel until he reached the age of 110. Read Joshua's farewell speech to the people of Israel. Write down any new detail in his account of Israel's history that you had not read so far in this year's course. _____
_____
_____
_____
_____
_____

2. What verse gave Joshua's famous challenge to the people? _____

3. In Joshua 24:25-28, Joshua conducted a covenant ceremony with Israel. From our past studies, which of the elements of covenant listed below were mentioned in this passage? Circle the ones that apply and give the verses where they are found.

    a) two parties or partners present or represented_____

    b) specific covenant terms recorded_____

    c) sealed with blood sacrifice_____

    d) memorialized with some object_____

    e) exchange of clothing, gifts, or weaponry_____

    f) witnesses present_____

    g) meal shared_____

4. a) What three burials are mentioned in the last verses of Chapter 24? _____

    _____

    b) What is significant about the burial of the bones of Joseph? _____

    _____

    _____

    _____

5. In verse 31 it says that *"Israel served the Lord all the days of Joshua, and all the days of the elders who outlived Joshua, who had known all the works of the Lord which He had done for Israel."* History shows that we are always just one generation away from faithlessness or apostasy. On our part, what is necessary for Christian work to continue after the present leadership dies?

_____

_____

_____

_____

_____

6. Now take a few minutes to read your study notes for this lesson.

Notes

Wise Words From Joshua

Settling In
Joshua 22

Joshua 21 had ended with this statement: *"Not a word failed of any good thing which the Lord had spoken to the house of Israel. All came to pass."* God had kept His Word to Israel, and now Joshua turned to the 2 1/2 tribes who had kept their word to God. For several years Reuben, Gad, and the half-tribe of Manasseh had stationed troops west of the Jordan in Canaan to assist the rest of Israel in clearing out the country of enemy inhabitants. Back across the Jordan their own families and possessions had remained until they could return to establish their homes in that land. Joshua commended them on their past performance but warned them about the future temptation to forget the ways of their God because of the geographical barrier that would separate them from the rest of the nation.

> *The whole theme of the book of Joshua had been that obedience to God's Word brings opportunity for blessing while disobedience brings disaster. No one better than Joshua could teach that this was true.*

Obey God!

The whole theme of the book of Joshua had been that obedience to God's Word brings opportunity for blessing while disobedience brings disaster. No one better than Joshua could teach that this was true. So, with great emotion, before dismissing them to take the valuables won in battle back to their homes for their new lives, he warned the tribes once more: *"But take careful heed to do the commandment and the law which Moses the servant of the Lord commanded you, to love the Lord your God, to walk in all His ways, to keep His commandments, to hold fast to Him, and to serve Him with all your heart and with all your soul"* (Joshua 22:5).

Tribal Trouble

Once across the Jordan, the two and a half tribes felt more than a geographical separation from the rest of Israel. They missed the central place of worship at Shiloh with its altar. So, as a memorial of the original and as a model to teach their children, they built a "great impressive altar" on the Canaan side of the river, evidently visible from their side too. When the tribes in Canaan heard of it, they reacted in righteous anger over what they thought was their brothers' participation in rebellion against God. This response really was a remarkable change. So often before, they had not reacted strongly enough about sin in their midst and had endured much chastening by God because of their lack of response. The nation gathered for civil war at Shiloh, but to their credit, they first sent Phinehas, son of the High Priest Eleazar, to investigate. He had distinguished himself earlier as he reacted on behalf of the Lord's honor to stop the sexual immorality and idolatry of a fellow Israelite during the trouble Balaam caused at Baal Peor. Along with Phinehas went representatives from each of the tribes west of the Jordan.

Phinehas and his delegation reminded the two and a half tribes of the judgment Israel had endured because of the sin at Baal Peor and the sin of Achan. They did not want to be judged now because of the sin of these who had built a rival altar. To avoid such problems, Phinehas and the others asked them to come back to the other side of the Jordan and receive a portion of land to live on there.

Reuben, Gad, and Manasseh's half-tribe responded that they were not guilty of any false worship. In fact, they had only built the altar to keep them true to God's ways, as a reminder of the one and only true altar, and as a teaching tool for their children's religious training. They promised they would only worship properly by crossing the river with their offerings to worship at the tabernacle. Phinehas and his delegation were satisfied and reported to their waiting brothers. The dispute was settled without war, and the altar was named *"Witness"* because it would serve as a witness between the two settlements that *"the Lord is God"* (Joshua 22:34).

| **What Can We Learn?** | Separation often brings misunderstanding because of lack of communication. Without the facts, human imagination often |

draws its own conclusions, imagining the worst possible motive. If the 2 1/2 tribes had not stopped short of the Promised Land, this incident would not have happened. However, since they did, careful, deliberate communication was needed to maintain a healthy relationship with their relatives across the river. We still live in a very imperfect world and often have to endure situations where we or others have "stopped short" of God's perfect will. We are surrounded by divorce and other estrangements, lack of education or information, and know the frustration of being caught up in the "if onlys" or "you shouldn't haves" of life. But even these difficult situations can be improved if we are determined to communicate regularly with those who are affected by our decisions. How often could we avoid a problem by picking up the phone or making a personal visit to find out the facts in a situation that has upset us? How often have we wished someone had asked us about our motives before they had jumped to some fact-less conclusion that brought about trouble? God knows our thoughts before we even speak them, but our brothers and sisters need to hear us before they will understand. The wise James warned: *"Let every man be swift to hear, slow to speak, and slow to wrath; for the wrath of man does not produce the righteousness of God"* (James 1:19,20).

Separation often brings misunderstanding because of lack of communication. Without the facts, human imagination often draws its own conclusions, imagining the worst possible motive.

God knows our thoughts before we even speak them, but our brothers and sisters need to hear us before they will understand.

Joshua's Farewell
Joshua 23

Like Moses before him, Joshua used every opportunity to remind the people of the basic truths about their relationship to God.

1. God has been good to you.
2. God will continue to help you.
3. Your part is to obey all that is written in the book of Moses.
4. Do not give in to the temptation to join with other people in their false worship.
5. With God, your power is multiplied: *"One man of you shall chase a thousand, for the Lord your God is He who fights for you, as He has promised"* (verse 10).
6. If you ever turn away from God to false gods, you will be punished and you will *"perish quickly from the good land which He has given you."*

History Lesson
Joshua 24:1-18

At Shechem Joshua had a final lesson to teach Israel. It was a history lesson that was meant to remind them of the faithfulness of God and to encourage them to continue in faithful obedience to Him. From Father Abraham to the fiendish Amorites, Joshua traced their progress. Everything they had at that moment—their lands, cities, vineyards, and groves—had been a gift from God (verse 13). Now, he challenged them, *"...Serve the Lord! And if it seems evil to you to serve the Lord, choose for yourselves this day whom you will serve, whether the gods which your fathers served that were on the other side of the River, or the gods of the Amorites, in whose land you dwell. But as for me and my house, we will serve the Lord"* (Joshua 24:14,15).

Along with the law, God had provided a way for them to come to Him as the sinners that they were. With His way provided, they could repeat, "No, but we will serve the Lord."

The people replied to Joshua's passionate appeal, *"We also will serve the Lord, for He is our God."* In what, at first glance, seemed an odd response, Joshua replied, *"You cannot serve the Lord, for He is a holy God. He is a jealous God; He will not forgive your transgressions nor your sins."* Joshua spoke what we find in the New Testament to be true. We cannot please God by ourselves. *"There is none righteous, no, not one"* (Romans 3:10). We may want to and may try, but without Jesus' sacrifice in our place and without His life in us, we cannot please God. However, Israel had a sacrificial system in place even then that looked forward to Christ. Along with the law, God had provided a way for them to come to Him as the sinners that they were. With His way provided, they could repeat, *"No, but we will serve the Lord."*

Covenant Commitment
Joshua 24:19-28

Using the powerful symbolism of covenant, Joshua renewed their relationship with God by writing out their commitment and memorializing the occasion with a large stone. Even after this, they would often break their word, but their mighty Covenant God would never break His. As often as they would return by way of the sacrificial blood, His blessings to them would also return. The New Covenant, sealed by the blood of Jesus, the Perfect and Eternal Lamb of God, holds us securely in its bonds, once we have entered it by faith. We can pledge our loyalty to Him, knowing that He in us can make obedience possible moment by moment.

The End for Three
Joshua 24:29-33

The burials of 110-year-old Joshua, the High Priest Eleazar, and the bones of Joseph were recorded in this final chapter. Joseph's dying orders, centuries before, to bury his bones in Canaan, stirred the faith of generations of Israelites. Joseph had believed God would one day take Israel back home, and it had finally happened. The deaths of Joshua and Eleazar marked the end of an important era. The Lord's leaders died, but the Lord's work continued—at least as long as the elders who had been taught by Joshua lived. What happened in succeeding generations? The same thing that can happen in any nation when one generation fails to teach its children the truths about God. When people fail to know why they are required or expected to live a certain way, they soon dismiss traditions as out-dated and unnecessary, and ungodliness is allowed to replace righteousness. Generations following Joshua quickly forgot anything they had been taught. *"When all that generation had been gathered to their fathers, another generation arose after them who did not know the Lord nor the work which He had done for Israel"* (Judges 2:10). They left the truth of God and began to do "what was right in their own eyes" (Judges 21:25). The "new morality" of that day was the old lie of the Garden of Eden, "My will, not Thine!" That kind of thinking guaranteed disaster for the nation—and still does.

> *When people fail to know why they are required or expected to live a certain way, they soon dismiss traditions as out-dated and unnecessary, and ungodliness is allowed to replace righteousness.*

One Last Word

This year's survey of the "Early History of Israel" through the books of Exodus, Leviticus, Numbers, Deuteronomy, and Joshua, should have taught us one main thing: God is in charge. He has established a standard of right living that cannot be debated or changed. While man can never reach it on his own, God has made Himself available to empower man to serve and please Him. There is a God who Rules. We are not God. He is the Creator. We are the created. We must come to Him in the only way He has permitted: by faith in the substitutional sacrifice of His Son, Himself, on the cross, once in time. Beyond our ability to reason or understand, He chose to love us in our unloveliest state. Like Israel, He has a particular plan He wants to fulfill in each of our lives:

> *The "new morality" of that day was the old lie of the Garden of Eden, "My will, not Thine!" That kind of thinking guaranteed disaster for the nation—and still does.*

"When I was made in secret...
 Your eyes saw my substance, being yet unformed.
And in Your book they all were written,
 The days fashioned for me,
When as yet there were none of them" (Psalm 139:15,16).

Like Israel, He has provided us with Scripture and a Sacrifice. The Old Testament law and sacrificial system pointed forward in time to Calvary. By faith they believed God would bring the ultimate and eternal Savior, who would write the law in each heart. By faith, we look back to Calvary, believing Jesus is the One sent from God to put us into the everlasting covenant, where our sins and sicknesses are exchanged for His righteousness and healing; our debts are paid by His riches; and our selfishness is exchanged for His self-sacrificing love. This is the day to start living in your Promised Land. Choose this day whom you will serve and stay committed to passing on the truth you have learned to those around you.

How Much Do You Remember?

We've had quite a bit of variety in this year's course—everything from A-Z! (Well, almost, X required a bit of rearranging!) Give it your best effort. Circle the correct answer.

A. Israel's first scene of defeat under Joshua: Atlanta, Alibi, Ai

B. Metal used for the altar of burnt offering: Boron, Bronz, Bizwax

C. Spokesman for the minority party after spying in Canaan: Cain, Cab, Caleb

D. Tenth plague on Egypt: Diarrhea, Death of firstborn, Deermites

E. Ancestor of the Amalekites: Esau, Evelyn, Eglon

F. Seven of these could be attended in three trips: Farms, Feasts, Funerals

G. Focus of the first four commandments: God, Glory, Goodness

H. One of the plagues affecting crops: Honey, Heat, Hail

I. Sin of the Golden Calf: Ignorance, Itchiness, Idolatry

J. Moses' faithful servant: Jeremiah, Jezebel, Joshua

K. Pharaoh's position in Egypt: King, Kook, Knight

L. Passover sacrifice: Leeks, Lamb, Lettuce

M. Wood in the water: Miriam, Midian, Marah

N. Offered unholy fire: Nathan, Nadab, Nobody

O. Attitude is important in this: Originality, Observation, Obedience

P. Membership restricted: Promise Keepers, Priesthood, Presidency

Q. Wilderness menu item: Quail, Quinine, Nestle's Quick

R. Symbolized by purple: Rhythm, Royalty, Readiness

S. Coin of redemption: Span, Straw, Shekel

T. Mobile worship center: Toledo, Tabernacle, Taberah

U. Basic cause of disobedience: Ugliness, Urban living, Unbelief

V. A binding promise: Vice, Vow, Valentine

W. Acacia was the kind in the tabernacle: Wood, Wax, Water

X. Number of cities of refuge: 26, 56, 6

Y. Leavening agent: Yodeling, Yeast, Yanking

Z. Had daughters who lobbied for women's rights: Zelophehad, Zulu, Zenoble

(If you need some extra help, see next page for Scripture references and answers!)

Answers to A-Z Review

A. Ai: Joshua 7:4

B. Bronze: Exodus 27:2

C. Caleb: Numbers 13:30

D. Death of firstborn: Exodus 11:5

E. Esau: Genesis 36:12

F. Feasts: Leviticus 23

G. God: Exodus 20

H. Hail: Exodus 9:18

I. Idolatry: Exodus 32:4

J. Joshua: Exodus 24:13

K. King: Exodus 1:8

L. Lamb: Exodus 12:21

M. Marah: Exodus 15:23 and 25

N. Nadab: Leviticus 10:1

O. Obedience: Deuteronomy 30:20

P. Priesthood: Exodus 40:15

Q. Quail: Exodus 16:13 and Numbers 11:31

R. Royalty: tradition

S. Shekel: Exodus 30:13

T. Tabernacle: Exodus 25:9

U. Unbelief: Deuteronomy 1:32

V. Vow: Numbers 6:2

W. Wood: Exodus 25:5

X. Six: Numbers 35:13

Y. Yeast: Exodus 12:15 NIV

Z. Zelophehad: Numbers 27